M000073944

承诺

不论身处日本、美国、中国或欧洲，我们的独立评审员均使用一致的评选方法对餐厅和酒店作出评估。米其林指南在世界各地均享负盛名，关键在其秉承一贯宗旨，履行对读者的承诺：

评审员以匿名方式定期到访餐厅和酒店，以一般顾客的身份对餐厅和酒店的食品和服务素质作出评估。评审员自行结账后，在需要时会介绍自己，并会详细询问有关餐厅或酒店的资料。

为保证本指南以读者利益为依归，餐厅的评选完全是我们独立的决定。我们不会向收录在指南内的餐厅收取任何费用，所有评选经编辑和评审员一同讨论才作出决定，最高级别的评级以国际水平为标准。

本指南推介一系列优质餐厅和酒店，当中含括不同的舒适程度和价格，这全赖一众评审员使用一致且严谨的评选方法。

所有实用资讯、分类及评级都会每年修订和更新，务求为读者提供最可靠的资料。

为确保指南的一致性，每个国家地区均采用相同的评审和分类准则，纵然各地的饮食文化不同，我们评选时的准则完全取决于食物素质和厨师的厨艺。

米其林的目标多年来贯彻始终 —— 致力令旅程尽善尽美，让您在旅游和外出用膳时不但安全，且充满乐趣。

THE MICHELIN GUIDE'S COMMITMENTS

Whether they are in Japan, the USA, China or Europe, our inspectors apply the same criteria to judge the quality of each and every restaurant and hotel that they visit. The MICHELIN guide commands a **worldwide reputation** thanks to the commitments we make to our readers – and we reiterate these below:

Our inspectors make regular and **anonymous visits** to restaurants and hotels to gauge the quality of products and services offered to an ordinary customer. They settle their own bill and may then introduce themselves and ask for more information about the establishment.

To remain totally objective for our readers, the selection is made with complete **independence**. Entry into the guide is free. All decisions are discussed with the Editor and our highest awards are considered at an international level.

The guide offers a **selection** of the best restaurants and hotels in every category of comfort and price. This is only possible because all the inspectors rigorously apply the same methods.

All the practical information, classifications and awards are revised and updated every year to give the most **reliable information** possible.

In order to guarantee the **consistency** of our selection, our classification criteria are the same in every country covered by the MICHELIN guide. Each culture may have its own unique cuisine but **quality** remains the **universal principle** behind our selection.

Michelin's mission is to **aid your mobility**. Our sole aim is to make your journeys safe and pleasurable.

米其林指南在上海
THE MICHELIN GUIDE IN SHANGHAI

不论是巷弄间的本帮老上海风味，还是摩天大楼内璀璨华灯下的欧陆佳肴，上海的餐厅总是绚丽多姿地展现大都会的万种风情。

米其林指南踏足上海第三年，评审们乐见更多不同菜系的优质餐厅在此地扎根，和不少别具个性的酒店开幕。指南同时亦作出革新，以更大的开本、更时尚的设计和新的编排与读者见面。

一如既往，米其林评审团队过去一年马不停蹄地追寻此城精彩美食，罗列在指南内的餐厅，不论价格高低、历史长短，均以高质的食物水平得到评审员肯定，当中包括了闻名的米其林星级餐厅❀、物超所值的必比登美食推介⊛，还有代表材料新鲜、烹调用心的米其林餐盘推介⊙。指南同时也挑选了一系列优质酒店，从时尚型格到豪华典雅，包含各个级别和种类。

若对本指南有任何意见，欢迎电邮至：michelinguide.shanghai@michelin.com

冀盼读者在上海享受到更精彩的美食和住宿体验。

With great pleasure, we present the third edition of Michelin Guide Shanghai, which comes with bigger pages, modern graphics and a new layout.

Within these pages you will discover the best restaurants across all categories of style and price. From authentic Shanghainese fare served in traditional restaurants tucked deep in rustic alleyways to contemporary European cuisine presented in opulent dining rooms atop modern skyscrapers, the restaurant scene in Shanghai is multifaceted and mesmerising, just like the alluring metropolis itself.

As always, our Michelin Inspectors have spent the past year searching the city for restaurants serving top quality food. Our famous Michelin Stars ❀ are awarded to those offering truly exceptional cooking but look out too for our Bib Gourmands ⊛, which offers carefully prepared but simpler cooking for under RMB 200. The Michelin Plate ⊙ then identifies all of our other restaurants, where you are guaranteed to have a good meal.

Our independent inspectors have also selected some outstanding hotels, from the hip and fashionable to the luxurious and elegant – all of which offer unique experiences.

Your opinions and suggestion help shape the guide, so please get in touch at: michelinguide.shanghai@michelin.com

We hope you enjoy your dining and hotel experiences in Shanghai.

目录
CONTENTS

黄浦区
HUANGPU
P. 24

静安区
JINGAN
P. 108

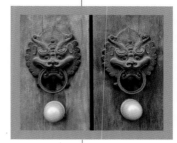

长宁区
CHANGNING
P. 140

徐汇及闵行区
XUHUI & MINHANG
P. 154

虹口区
HONGKOU
P. 180

浦东新区
PUDONG
P. 192

从前，在法国中部

这一切始于1889年，米其林兄弟在法国克莱蒙费朗 (Clermont-Ferrand) 创办Manufacture Française des Pneumatiques Michelin 轮胎公司——当年驾驶汽车仍被视为一大冒险。

在1900年，法国的汽车总数量少于3,000辆。米其林兄弟灵机一触，想到为道路驾驶的先驱提供含实用资讯的小指南，如补充汽油或更换轮胎，以至用餐和睡觉的好去处。米其林指南就这样诞生了！

指南的宗旨非常清晰：搜罗全国各地最好的酒店和餐厅。为达目的，米其林招揽了一整队神秘专业评审员，走遍全国每一个角落寻找值得推介的酒店和餐厅，这在当时是前所未有的创举。

多年来，崎岖不平的道路早已被平顺的高速公路取代，米其林公司持续茁壮成长。同时间，全国各地餐饮业的发展亦一日千里：厨子成为大厨、传统手艺成为艺术，传统菜亦转化成为艺术杰作。现今米其林指南已成为广受信赖的旅游伙伴，不仅与时并进，更致力推动这些转变。指南中最著名的是早在1926年面世，并迅即成为美食界权威指标的"星级推介"。

由米其林轮胎人必比登为代言人的米其林指南，不断拓展其版图，到1911年已覆盖全欧洲。

2006年，米其林指南系列成功跨越大西洋，授予纽约39家餐厅星级推介。在2007及2008年，米其林指南在三藩市、洛杉矶和拉斯维加斯出版，2011年已拓展至芝加哥，米其林必比登也正式落户美国。

2007年11月，米其林轮胎人首次踏足亚洲，在东京广发星级推介，以表扬日本料理的卓越成就，同时亦掀起美食热潮。其后，旋即推出京都、神户、大阪及奈良指南，并继东京之后推出横滨和湘南指南。香港和澳门指南亦于2009年推出。

2016年，必比登更涉足新加坡、中国和韩国，并在2018年踏足泰国，令这本以红色为标志的指南，在远东地区的覆盖范围更见广泛。

时至今日，米其林指南系列共计32本，涵盖30个国家，一个世纪以来，总销量超过三千万册。这是个令人鼓舞的纪录！

此时此刻，我们仍然继续对美食的追寻……是巴黎餐厅的美味杂菜锅，还是令人垂涎的红烧肉？必比登将会努力不懈，发掘全球美食，为你们挑选最出色的佳肴美馔！

ONCE UPON A TIME, IN THE HEART OF FRANCE...

It all started way back in 1889, in Clermont-Ferrand, when the Michelin brothers founded the Manufacture Française des Pneumatiques Michelin tyre company – this was at a time when driving was considered quite an adventure!

In 1900, fewer than 3,000 cars existed in France. The Michelin brothers hit upon the idea of creating a small guide packed with useful information for the new pioneers of the road, such as where to fill up with petrol or change a tyre, as well as where to eat and sleep. The MICHELIN Guide was born!

The purpose of the guide was obvious: to track down the best hotels and restaurants across the country. To do this, Michelin employed a veritable armada of anonymous professional inspectors to scour every region – something that had never before been attempted!

Over the years, bumpy roads were replaced by smoother highways and the company continued to develop, as indeed did the country's cuisine: cooks became chefs, artisans developed into artists, and traditional dishes were transformed into works of art. All the while, the MICHELIN Guide, by now a faithful travel companion, kept pace with – and encouraged – these changes. The most famous distinction awarded by the guide was created in 1926: the "étoile de bonne table" – the famous star which quickly established itself as the reference in the world of gastronomy!

Bibendum – the famous tyre-clad Michelin man – continued to widen his reach and by 1911, the guide covered the whole of Europe.

In 2006, the collection crossed the Atlantic, awarding stars to 39 restaurants in New York. In 2007 and 2008, the guide moved on to San Francisco, Los Angeles and Las Vegas, and in 2011 it was the turn of Chicago to have its own Michelin guide – The Michelin Man had become truly American!

In November 2007, The Michelin Man took his first steps in Asia: in recognition of the excellence of Japanese cuisine, stars rained down on Tokyo, which was gripped by culinary fever! A guide to Kyoto, Kobe, Osaka and Nara followed, with Yokohama and Shonan then joining Tokyo. Thereafter the Michelin Man set his feet down in Southern China, with the publication in 2009 of a guide to Hong Kong and Macau.

The Red Guide was now firmly on the map in the Far East. The Michelin Man then explored Southeast Asia and China. In 2016 the first edition of MICHELIN Guides Singapore, Shanghai and Seoul were published. In 2018, the Michelin Man further set foot in Thailand. The collection now covers 32 titles in 30 countries, with over 30 million copies sold in a century. Quite a record!

Meanwhile, the search continues... Looking for a delicious cassoulet or pot-au-feu in a typical Parisian bistro, or tempting braised pork belly in Shanghai? The Michelin Man continues to span the globe making new discoveries and selecting the very best the culinary world has to offer!

米其林美食评级分类 ────

星级美食

闻名遐迩的米其林一星✽、二星✽✽和三星✽✽✽推介,推荐的是
食物素质特别出色的餐厅。我们的评级考虑到以下因素:材料的
素质和搭配、烹调技巧和味道层次、菜肴所展示的创意,少不了
的是食物水平的一致性。

✽✽✽　　卓越的烹调,值得专程造访。
✽✽　　　烹调出色,不容错过!
✽　　　　优质烹调,不妨一试!

必比登美食推介餐厅

必比登标志表示该餐厅提供具素质且
经济实惠的美食:费用在200元或以下
(三道菜式但不包括饮料)。

米其林餐盘

评审员万里挑一的餐厅,
食材新鲜、烹调用心,菜肴美味。

米其林图标

米其林是追寻最佳餐厅的专家，邀请您共同发掘丰富多元的餐饮世界。在品评餐厅烹调素质同时，我们亦将其装潢、服务和整体氛围加入考虑，换言之，是包含味觉、感官和整体用餐经验的全方位评估。

两组关键词助你挑选合适的餐厅，红色为菜式种类；金色是环境氛围：

沪菜 · *典雅*

设施及服务

🚫💳	只接受现金
🚫💳	不接受国际信用卡
♿	轮椅通道
🏠	阳台用餐
≼	上佳景观
🅿	代客泊车
P	停车场
🚗	室内停车场
⊞12	私人厢房及座位数目
▭	柜台式
☏🍴	需订座
🚫🍴	不设订座
🚭	非吸烟房
👥	会议室
🏊 🏊	室内 / 室外游泳池
Spa	水疗服务
🏋	健身室
🍇	供应优质餐酒

THE MICHELIN GUIDE'S SYMBOLS

Michelin are experts at finding the best restaurants and invite you to explore the diversity of the gastronomic universe. As well as evaluating a restaurant's cooking, we also consider its décor, the service and the ambience – in other words, the all-round culinary experience.

Two keywords help you make your choice more quickly: red for the type of cuisine, gold for the atmosphere:

Shanghainese • Elegant

FACILITIES & SERVICES

	Cash only
	International credit cards not accepted
	Wheelchair access
	Terrace dining
	Interesting view
	Valet parking
	Car park
	Garage
12	Private room with maximum capacity
	Counter
	Reservations required
	Reservations not accepted
	Non smoking rooms
	Conference rooms
	Indoor / Outdoor swimming pool
	Spa
	Exercise room
	Interesting wine list

THE MICHELIN DISTINCTIONS FOR GOOD CUISINE

STARS

Our famous One ❀, Two ❀❀ and Three ❀❀❀ Stars
identify establishments serving the highest quality
cuisine – taking into account the quality of ingredients,
the mastery of techniques and flavours, the levels of
creativity and, of course, consistency.

❀❀❀	Exceptional cuisine, worth a special journey!
❀❀	Excellent cuisine, worth a detour!
❀	High quality cooking, worth a stop!

BIB GOURMAND

This symbol indicates our inspectors'
favourites for good value. These restaurants
offer quality cooking for ¥200 or less
(price of a 3 course meal excluding drinks).

PLATE

Good cooking.
Fresh ingredients, capably prepared:
simply a good meal.

上海
SHANGHAI

0   2 km

West Guangzhong Rd
广中西路

上海马戏城
Shanghai Circus World

新村路
Xincun Rd

Hutai Rd

延长路
Yanchang Rd

延长路
Yanchang Rd

交通路 Jiaotong Rd

铜川路 Tongchuan Rd

岚皋路
Langao Rd

中潭路
Zhongtan Rd

真如
Zhenru

上海火车站
Shanghai Railway Station

普陀区
PUTUO

武宁路 Wuning Rd

曹杨路
Caoyang Rd

镇坪路
Zhenping Rd

梦清园
Mengqing Garden

天目西路
Tianmu Xi Rd

枫桥路
Fengqiao Rd

长寿路
Changshou Rd

汉中路
Hanzhong Rd

Bishong Rd 北虹路

金沙江路
Jinshajiang Rd

宁夏路
Ningxia Rd

沪西大剧院
Huxi Theater

隆德路
Longde Rd

静安区
JINGAN

Dadube Rd 大渡河路

长风公园
Changfeng Park

万航渡路
Wanhangdu Rd

南京西路
West Nanjing Rd

陕西南路
Shaanxi Rd. (S)

吴淞江
Wusong River

中山公园
Zhongshan Park

静安寺
Jing'an Temple

淮海中路
Huaihai Rd

Danba Rd 丹巴路

江苏路
Jiangsu Rd

West Yan'an Rd 延安西路

常熟路
Changshu Rd

Changning Rd

中山公园
Zhongshan Park

长宁区
CHANGNING

天山路 Tianshan Rd

延安西路
Yan'an Rd. (W)

新华路 Xinhua Rd

淮海路 Huaihai Rd

衡山路
Hengshan Rd

Hengshan Rd 肇嘉浜路
Zhaojiabang Rd

上海国际展览中心
Shanghai International Exhibition Center

上海城市雕塑艺术中心
Shanghai Sculpture Space

虹桥路
Hongqiao Rd

华山路 Huashan Rd

Dong'an Rd 东安路

虹桥路 Hongqiao Rd

虹桥路 Hongqiao Rd

凯旋路 Kaixuan Rd

Hongqiao Rd

徐家汇
Xujiahui

东安路
Dong'an Rd

宋庆龄墓
Song Qingling Cemetery

上海电影博物馆
Shanghai Film Museum

上海体育场
Shanghai Stadium

宜山路
Yishan Rd

上海体育馆
Shanghai Indoor Stadium

龙华路 Longhua Rd

漕溪路
Caoxi Rd

上海体育场
Shanghai Stadium

虹桥路 Hongqiao Rd

徐汇区
XUHUI

龙漕路
Longcao Rd

龙华
Longhua

龙华烈士陵园
Longhua Martyrs Cemetery

闵行区
MINHANG

Wuzhong Rd

桂平路 Guiping Rd

虹漕路

漕宝路
Caobao Rd

龙华港
Longhuagang River

Caoxi Rd

龙华路

上海南站
Shanghai South Station

West Yan'an Rd 延安西路

虹桥路 Hongqiao Rd

中山西路 West Zhongshan Rd

延安西路

普汇塘河
Puhuitang River

Guangzhong Rd
West Dalian Rd
大连西路
鲁迅公园
Lu Xun Park
上海鲁迅故居
Former Residence
of Lu Xun
杨浦公园
YANGPU PARK
虹口足球场
Hongkou
Football Stadium
和平公园
PEACE
PARK
多伦路
Duolun Road
多伦现代美术馆
Duolun Museum
of Modern Art
临平路
Linping
Rd
大连路 Changyang
Dalian Rd
Pingliang Rd
西藏北路
Xizang North Rd
海伦路
Hailun Rd
大连路
Dalian Rd
中山北路北
Zhongshan Rd. (N)
东宝兴路
Dongbaoxing Rd
宝山路
Baoshan
Rd
1933老场坊
1933 Laoyangfang
霍山公园
Huoshan
Park
杨浦大桥
Yangpu Bridge
兴 路
海宁路
Haining Rd
虹口区
HONGKOU
Dong Da Ming Rd
成都
北路
新闸路
Xinzha Rd
North
Xizang Rd
东大名 路
国际客运码头
INTERNATIONAL
PASSENGER TERMINAL
Pudong Avenue
南京东路
北京东路 East Beijing
Nanjing Rd. (E)
黄浦公园
Huangpu Park
外滩
The Bund
上海海洋水族馆
Shanghai Ocean Aquarium
陆家嘴
Lujiazui
浦 东 大
West
Beijing Rd
North Chengdu Rd
人民广场
人民广场
People's
People's Sq
Square
上海博物馆
SHANGHAI
MUSEUM
豫园
Yuyuan Garden
上海环球金融中心
Shanghai World
Financial Center
上海国际金融中心
Shanghai IFC
昌邑路
Dongchang Rd
道
南京西路
Nanjing
Rd. (W.)
延安东路
East Yan'an
上海音乐厅
Shanghai
Concert Hall
民 路
Min Rd
商城路
Shangcheng Rd
世纪大道
Century Avenue
Middle Yan'an
黄陂南路
Huangpi Rd (S)
豫园
Yu Garden
黄浦区
HUANGPU
世纪大道
Weifang Rd
Century
Avenue
上海东方艺术中心
Oriental Art Center
Middle
淮海中路南
Huaihai Rd (M)
新天地
Xintiandi
Fuxing
新天地
Xintiandi
Zhonghua
Zhongshan Rd
浦电路
Pudian Rd
Pudian
上海科技馆
Shanghai Science &
Technology Museum
上海科技馆
Shanghai Science &
Technology Museum
世纪公园
CENTURY PARK
兴
West Jianguo Rd
马当路
Madang Rd
陆家浜路
Lujiabang Rd
小南门
Xiaonanmen
南浦大桥
Nanpu
Bridge
S. Pudong Rd
塘桥
Tangqiao
蓝村路
Lancun Rd
花木路
Huamu Rd
锦
徐
汇
路
Xujiahui Rd
西藏南路
Xizang
Rd. (S)
南浦大桥
Nanpu
Bridge
上海儿童医学中心
Shanghai Children's
Medical Center
建 路 Pujian
磁浮列车
MAGLEV TRAIN
绣
嘉善路
Jiashan Rd
瑞金路
Ruijin Rd
South Chongqing Rd
鲁班路
Luban Rd
South Zhongshan Rd
三山会馆
Sanshan Guild Hall
临沂新村
Linyi Xincun
龙
阳
Longyang Rd
路
中
山
世博会博物馆
World Expo Museum
世博大道
Shibo Ave
Pudong Rd
黄
浦
Lupu
Bridge
Lupu
打浦路隧道
中华艺术宫
China Art Museum
高科西路
Gaoke Rd (W)
博 文 路 Bowen Rd
Jinxiu Rd
世博大道
Shibo Ave
EXPO CENTRE
世博大道
Shibo Ave
云台路
Yuntai Road
中华艺术宫
China Art Museum
Huangpu River
长清路
Changqing Rd
耀华路
Yaohua
Rd
东明路
Dongming Rd
成山路
Chengshan Rd
后滩
Houtan
昌 里 路
成 山 路
Chengshan
Changli Rd
川 杨 河
Fengxi Rd
Yaolong Rd
成山路
Chengshan Rd
Chuanyang River
浦东新区
PUDONG
上海植物园
Shanghai Botanical Garden

N

餐厅和酒店...以地区分类
RESTAURANTS & HOTELS...
OUR SELECTION BY DISTRICT

Adstock/Universal Images Group / age fotostock

黄浦区

HUANGPU

黄浦区 **HUANGPU**

RESTAURANTS
餐厅

✿ ✿ ✿

ULTRAVIOLET BY PAUL PAIRET

创新菜·前卫

Innovative · Trendy

想试试神秘的用餐体验吗？你必先要提前在官方网站订座，且不介意和素不相识的人围坐一桌共享晚餐。在预定的日期和约定的地点，商务车会将你和一众食客送抵神秘之地，二十二道风味创新的菜式，伴随着出众的餐酒、特别设计的灯效影像及音乐，为你留下一段难忘的回忆。

After the enormous success of Mr & Mrs Bund, chef Paul Pairet created this clever concept 'somewhere in Shanghai'. The lucky 10 people who managed to secure an on-line reservation meet up at Mr & Mrs Bund and from there they are driven to the chosen venue and its communal table. Lights, sounds, music and innovative cuisine – this is an immersive, exclusive experience that's so much more than just a 22 course dinner.

  ⌨ ◐❚

黄浦区中山东一路18号外滩18号
6楼（集合地点）

'somewhere in Shanghai' –
meet at Mr & Mrs Bund restaurant –
6F, Bund 18,
18 Zhongshan Dong Yi Road,
Huangpu

www.uvbypp.cc

■ 价钱 **PRICE**
晚膳 Dinner
套餐 set ￥4,000-6,000

■ 营业时间 **OPENING HOURS**
晚膳 Dinner 从 From 18:30

■ 休息日期 **ANNUAL AND WEEKLY CLOSING**
农历新年、10月1至7日、周日及周一休息
Closed Lunar New Year, October
1-7, Sunday and Monday

黄浦区 HUANGPU

黄浦区 HUANGPU

♿ 🅿 ⇄12 ◎🍴

TEL. 6733 7123

黄浦区汝南街63号
63 Runan Street, Huangpu

■ 价钱 **PRICE**
午膳 Lunch
套餐 set ¥ 300-500
点菜 à la carte ¥ 100-300
晚膳 Dinner
套餐 set ¥ 300-500
点菜 à la carte ¥ 200-500

■ 营业时间 **OPENING HOURS**
午膳 Lunch 11:00-14:00 (L.O.)
晚膳 Dinner 17:00-21:00 (L.O.)

■ 休息日期 **ANNUAL AND WEEKLY CLOSING**
农历新年6天及公众假期休息
Closed 6 days Lunar New Year and Public Holidays

❀❀

喜粤8号（汝南街）
CANTON 8 (RUNAN STREET)

粤菜·时尚

Cantonese · Contemporary décor

店东林先生富多年餐厅运营经验，开店的目标非常清晰：让食客以亲民的价格品尝到高素质的广东点心和小菜。在厨房领军的简师傅掌厨逾五十年，经验丰富，更不时花心思更新菜单，以求为客人带来新鲜感。餐单菜式不多却简而精，除了炖汤、烧味、小炒和五花八门的鱼类菜式，甜点更是不容错过。

This is the place to go for quality dim sum and classic Cantonese fare at affordable prices. The head chef has over 50 years of experience in Cantonese cooking. The menu is not overly long but is updated regularly, showcasing the quintessence of the cuisine alongside newer dishes. Apart from double-boiled soups, roast meats, stir-fries and a myriad of fish dishes, the desserts are also unmissable.

御宝轩
IMPERIAL TREASURE
粤菜 · 经典

Cantonese · Classic

来自新加坡的御宝集团餐饮种类多元化,设于益丰·外滩源的这家提供各式高级粤菜,如海鲜、汤品、烧味和点心,食物水准上乘,不论是功夫菜如糯米炸子鸡或简单的云吞面,均做得正宗而精细,尽显厨师手艺。建议订座时预留大热的炖汤和烧味。环境同样一丝不苟,餐室以黑色作主调,配以大量水晶,格调优雅。

The Imperial Treasure Group from Singapore has a diverse catering portfolio – this restaurant of theirs at Yi Feng Galleria focuses on Cantonese cuisine. The dining room, a worthy match for the food, is elegantly dressed with plenty of crystal. The kitchen prepares the cuisine in a traditional style, whether that's something simple like wonton noodles or dishes that require much more preparation such as crispy chicken with glutinous rice.

P ⇔20 ☺⚟
TEL. 5308 1188
黄浦区北京东路99号
益丰·外滩源4楼
**4F, Yi Feng Galleria,
99 East Beijing Road, Huangpu**

■ 价钱 PRICE
午膳 Lunch
点菜 à la carte ¥ 200-250
晚膳 Dinner
点菜 à la carte ¥ 250-500

■ 营业时间 OPENING HOURS
午膳 Lunch 11:00-14:30 (L.O.)
周末午膳 Weekend lunch
11:00-15:00 (L.O.)
晚膳 Dinner 17:00-22:15 (L.O.)

黄浦区 HUANGPU

HUANGPU 黄浦区

<€ 🍴 ⌀10 🚗 ☺️🍴 ⚅

TEL. 6071 8888

黄浦区中山东一路18号外滩18号3楼

**3F, Bund 18,
18 Zhongshan Dong Yi Road,
Huangpu**
www.joelrobuchon-china.com

■ 价钱 **PRICE**
午膳 Lunch
套餐 set ¥ 688-1,498
点菜 à la carte ¥ 600-1,500
晚膳 Dinner
套餐 set ¥ 688-1,498
点菜 à la carte ¥ 600-1,500

■ 营业时间 **OPENING HOURS**
周末午膳 Weekend lunch
11:30-14:00 (L.O.)
晚膳 Dinner 17:30-22:30 (L.O.)

■ 休息日期 **ANNUAL AND WEEKLY
CLOSING**
农历新年休息
Closed Lunar New Year

✿ ✿

乔尔·卢布松美食坊
L'ATELIER DE JOËL ROBUCHON

时尚法国菜·典雅
French contemporary · Elegant

法籍厨师乔尔·卢布松在全球的第十二家店子，位于外滩十八号这幢富有历史意义的大楼内。装潢格调与其姊妹店无异，非常时尚气派。经典的法国菜渗着点点现代风味，细腻精湛的厨艺已令用餐层次升华至味觉的艺术体验。用餐前不妨点杯鸡尾酒，顺道欣赏外滩景色。餐厅新添了价格更大众化的四道菜餐单，专供柜台座位享用。

Just like other branches around the world, this one boasts the iconic red-and-black colour scheme and a counter wrapped around an open kitchen. A highly skilled kitchen team prepare the sublime French cuisine with clever modern touches, accuracy and aplomb. Sitting at the counter not only lets you watch the alchemy unfold, but also entitles you to order from an exclusively discounted set menu. Arrive early to sip a cocktail and take in the views.

8 ½ OTTO E MEZZO BOMBANA

意大利菜 · 豪华

Italian · Luxury

位于洛克·外滩源，布置雅致时尚。高端精致的鸡尾酒吧、能饱览壮丽的黄浦江景色的阳台，视觉上的享受已让你感到惬意。厨艺精湛且富经验的厨房团队，选用高素质食材制作传统经典菜式，并巧妙地替菜式添了点现代元素。高质量的酒单和出色的服务，令用餐体验倍添美妙。

The third restaurant under the aegis of chef Umberto Bombana, after Hong Kong and Macau, occupies the top floor of a restored building in the Rockbund development area. The chic space comes with a cocktail bar and a balcony with jaw-dropping views of the Huangpu River. The kitchen delivers well-judged, classic Italian food using top quality ingredients. Along with highly skilled cooking, you can expect impeccable service and an impressive wine list.

☞ 🍷 ⌂30 🍴 🎎
TEL. 6087 2890
黄浦区圆明园路169号协进大楼6楼
6F, Associate Mission Building,
169 Yuanmingyuan Road, Huangpu
www.ottoemezzobombana.com

■ 价钱 **PRICE**
晚膳 Dinner
套餐 set ¥ 1,388
点菜 à la carte ¥ 450-1,320

■ 营业时间 **OPENING HOURS**
晚膳 Dinner 18:00-23:00 (L.O.)

■ 休息日期 **ANNUAL AND WEEKLY CLOSING**
农历新年休息7天
Closed 7 days Lunar New Year

黄浦区 **HUANGPU**

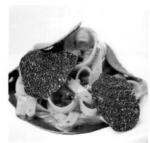

♿ 🅿 🛏14 ⊙📶 ♨

TEL. 2330 2288

黄浦区新天地马当路99号
朗廷酒店5楼

**5F, The Langham, 99 Madang Road,
Xintiandi, Huangpu**

www.xintiandi.langhamhotels.com

■ 价钱 **PRICE**
午膳 Lunch
套餐 set ￥588-1,588
点菜 à la carte ￥270-1,190
晚膳 Dinner
套餐 set ￥888-1,588
点菜 à la carte ￥270-1,190

■ 营业时间 **OPENING HOURS**
午膳 Lunch 11:30-14:00 (L.O.)
晚膳 Dinner 17:30-22:00 (L.O.)

❀ ❀

唐阁

T'ANG COURT

粤菜・型格

Cantonese • Design

盘旋曲折的走廊上，布满私人厢房；主餐室只有六张
布得得一丝不苟的餐桌。专业的服务团队配合高素质
的食物，让用餐成为美妙愉快的经历！餐单上是经典
与现代风味融合而成的粤菜，令人印象深刻。新加入
的厨师团队为餐厅带来新气象，白雪藏金龙和脆百合
炒和牛粒都是其得意之作。包厢只供应套餐。

After passing along the gorgeous curved
corridor of private rooms, you may feel that
the main dining room, with just six formally
dressed tables, is a little understated. However,
the charm and professionalism of the staff will
soon put you at ease. The newly joined chef
delivers a mix of classic and modern Cantonese
dishes. Specialities include braised red lobster
with sea urchin and braised fish maw with crab
roe. Private rooms serve a set menu only.

逸龙阁
YI LONG COURT

粤菜·豪华
Cantonese · luxury

半岛酒店旗下的旗舰粤菜餐馆，装潢布置以1930年代上海菜馆的风格为骨干，将典雅、细致与奢华融合于一。由富多年经验的香港主厨设计的菜单内全是经典粤菜，不妨试试黑豚肉叉烧及煎焗沙姜乳鸽脯。私人厢房布置得美仑美奂，甚有旧上海靡丽之风。

The Peninsula hotel's flagship restaurant provides luxurious dining in an elegant, urbane space inspired by 1930s Shanghai. The menu of Cantonese classics is prepared by a chef with many years of experience in Hong Kong – one of the dishes to go for is the barbecued Iberico pork. The individually furnished private rooms are beautiful to behold; and to fully experience the culinary craft here, consider booking the Chef's Table.

♿ ♻ ☏ 60 ☏ ♻

TEL. 2327 2888
黄浦区中山东一路32号外滩32号
半岛酒店2楼
2F, The Peninsula Hotel, Bund 32,
32 Zhongshan Dong Yi Road,
Huangpu

www.peninsula.com/shanghai

■ 价钱 **PRICE**
午膳 Lunch
点菜 à la carte ¥ 450-750
晚膳 Dinner
点菜 à la carte ¥ 1,000-1,500

■ 营业时间 **OPENING HOURS**
午膳 Lunch 11:30-14:30 (L.O.)
晚膳 Dinner 18:00-22:30 (L.O)

黄浦区 **HUANGPU**

≼ 🍷 🚱 ⓞ🍴 ♨

TEL. 5383 3656

黄浦区广东路20号外滩5号6楼

6F, Bund 5, 20 Guangdong Road, Huangpu

■ 价钱 **PRICE**
晚膳 Dinner
套餐 set ￥1,680

■ 营业时间 **OPENING HOURS**
晚膳 Dinner 18:00-21:30 (L.O.)

■ 休息日期 **ANNUAL AND WEEKLY CLOSING**
农历新年7天、周一及周二休息
Closed 7 days Lunar New Year, Monday and Tuesday

BO SHANGHAI

创新菜 · 型格

Innovative · Design

穿过厨魔馆后那短小而满布破烂瓷器餐具的小通道，推开趟门便仿如走进另一个空间 —— 爵士风格的华语音乐悠悠扬起，气氛轻松，你即将体验一个以各地食材炮制，将中国大江南北经典菜式共冶一炉的味觉旅程。包含十二道菜的餐单完美地呈现主厨对食物的热诚，服务无微不至更是锦上添花。

Tucked behind Daimon Gastrolounge, Bo Shanghai is a speakeasy-style outpost of the celebrated Hong Kong fine-dining concept Bo Innovation. Diners are escorted behind a sliding wall through a glass hallway above broken clay pots into a serene wood-clad dining hall. Service is attentive and the attention-grabbing 12-course tasting menus designed to reflect the eight silos of Chinese cuisine change every three months.

JEAN GEORGES

法国菜·典雅
French · Elegant

由法国厨师Jean Georges开设，2016年翻新过的餐室时尚、雅致且有气派。套餐餐单和装修前一样跟随着纽约总店的步伐，经典菜式如鸡蛋鱼子酱、黄旗金枪鱼等均在其上。美酒配佳肴，搜罗自世界各地的酒单内有逾七百款优秀餐酒。

Celebrated French chef Jean-Georges Vongerichten's restaurant opened in 2004 but got a new look in 2016. White and beige tones, a lovely bar and lounge facing an open kitchen and an elegant dining room make eating here something a little special. The menus feature many dishes from the mother ship in NYC: toasted egg yolk with caviar, yellow tuna ribbons; and red snapper with seeds. To complement the cuisine is a wine list of over 700 labels.

TEL. 6321 7733
黄浦区中山东一路3号外滩3号4楼
4F, Bund 3,
3 Zhongshan Dong Yi Road, Huangpu
www.threeonthebund.com

■ 价钱 **PRICE**
午膳 Lunch
套餐 set ￥298-998
点菜 à la carte ￥400-1,200
晚膳 Dinner
套餐 set ￥698-1,498
点菜 à la carte ￥600-1,400

■ 营业时间 **OPENING HOURS**
午膳 Lunch 11:30-14:30 (L.O.)
晚膳 Dinner 18:00-22:30 (L.O.)

黄浦区 **HUANGPU**

♿ 20 🅾

TEL. 6322 2624

黄浦区福州路556号
556 Fuzhou Road, Huangpu

- **价钱 PRICE**
午膳 Lunch
点菜 à la carte ¥ 100-200
晚膳 Dinner
点菜 à la carte ¥ 100-300

- **营业时间 OPENING HOURS**
午膳 Lunch 11:00-14:00 (L.O.)
晚膳 Dinner 17:00-21:00 (L.O.)

老正兴（黄浦）
LAO ZHENG XING (HUANGPU)

沪菜・简朴
Shanghainese・Simple

始于1862年的老正兴，是上海历史最悠久的本帮菜馆，多年来享誉海内外，不少经典名菜均出于此，是探索正宗本帮菜味道的不二之选。1997年迁至现址后，环境宽敞舒适，主餐室和包厢分布在各个楼层。油爆虾、虾籽大乌参等是招牌菜之一，欲多尝数道招牌菜，便要多约几位同伴前来。

Known locally and internationally since its inception in 1862, Lao Zheng Xing is reputedly the oldest Shanghainese restaurant in the city and was responsible for creating a number of classic dishes. It moved to its current location in 1997, which gave it considerably more space as it now occupies several floors. Come with friends to enjoy signature dishes like fried river shrimps and braised sea cucumber.

南麓·浙里（黄浦）
LE PATIO & LA FAMILLE (HUANGPU)

杭州菜·经典

Hangzhou · Classic

店子门面低调得很，一不留神很容易便错过。推门入内映入眼帘的是布置得像三十年代上海咖啡室的餐室，再往里走则是风格截然不同的时尚餐室。不论选择坐在哪，食客尝到的都是精致的杭帮菜。餐单不算长，精彩菜式却不少，西湖醋鱼、肘子老鸭煲和金牌扣肉都是例子，江南富贵鸡煲更值得预订。

The first time you come to this restaurant you may find yourself walking past a couple of times as its non-descript façade makes it easy to miss. The decorative style inside is influenced by the look of Shanghai's coffee shops in the 1930s – but, somewhat surprisingly, this is actually a Hangzhou restaurant. The dishes to try are steamed grass carp in vinegar sauce; pork trotter and duck casserole; and braised pork belly in soy sauce.

♿12 🅾️🍴

TEL. 6323 1797

黄浦区四川中路216号
216 Middle Sichuan Road, Huangpu

■ 价钱 **PRICE**
午膳 Lunch
点菜 à la carte ¥ 200-300
晚膳 Dinner
点菜 à la carte ¥ 200-300

■ 营业时间 **OPENING HOURS**
午膳 Lunch 11:00-14:00 (L.O.)
晚膳 Dinner 17:00-21:00 (L.O.)

黄浦区 **HUANGPU**

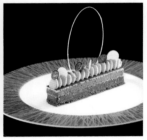

 ♿ ⟨ 🍷 ⛟14 🌸

TEL. 2327 2888

黄浦区中山东一路32号外滩32号
半岛酒店13楼

**13F, The Peninsula Hotel, Bund 32,
32 Zhongshan Dong Yi Road,
Huangpu**

www.peninsula.com/shanghai

■ 价钱 PRICE
午膳 Lunch
套餐 set ￥288
晚膳 Dinner
套餐 set ￥968-1,888
点菜 à la carte ￥700-1,800

■ 营业时间 OPENING HOURS
午膳 Lunch 12:00-14:30 (L.O.)
晚膳 Dinner 18:00-22:30 (L.O.)

❀

艾利爵士
SIR ELLY'S

时尚法国菜・典雅
French contemporary・Elegant

设于酒店顶层的艾利爵士餐厅，能遥望黄浦江两岸，景观开扬。布置典雅、细致的酒吧和装潢豪华的酒廊，还有天台酒吧动人心魄的城市美景，视觉上的享受让进餐体验变得完满。套餐分别由四、五或六道新颖菜式组合而成，食客可独立点选菜单上的食品。精选的餐酒是最佳的佐餐饮料。

Named after the hotel's founder, Sir Elly's occupies a commanding position on the 13th floor, with panoramic views across the river. However, the interior decoration still manages to compete for your attention, thanks to its impressive chandelier, opulent red hues and immaculately dressed tables. The chef delivers contemporary and sophisticated French cuisine, complemented by a substantial wine list.

大蔬无界（黄浦）
WUJIE (HUANGPU)

素食·型格

Vegetarian · Design

采用最时令的食材，以中国传统养生饮食作烹调基础制作出来的素食，打破了素菜予人平淡无味的观念，创新的煮意与国际化的烹调，偏向欧陆风味的菜式，带给你崭新的味蕾体验。室内装潢将江南园林元素与现代艺术融为一体，亦古典亦时尚，似要与身处的百岁欧陆建筑相互呼应。与其他分店不同，这店只供应套餐。

This branch of the vegetarian group occupies a century old European-style building on the Bund and the decoration draws on the spirit of Jiangnan Gardens combined with modern art to create a very pleasant atmosphere in which to dine. The kitchen blends various cooking techniques with Chinese philosophies of nourishment to create creative and beguiling vegetarian dishes for their loyal clientele. Only set menus will be served.

🍷 ♻24 ◎¶

TEL. 6375 2818

黄浦区中山东二路22号
外滩22号4楼405-407号

**405-407, 4F, Bund 22,
22 Zhongshan Dong Er Road,
Huangpu**

■ 价钱 **PRICE**
午膳 Lunch
套餐 set ¥ 399-799
晚膳 Dinner
套餐 set ¥ 399-799

■ 营业时间 **OPENING HOURS**
午膳 Lunch 11:00-14:00 (L.O.)
晚膳 Dinner 17:00-22:00 (L.O.)

黄浦区 **HUANGPU**

HUANGPU 黄浦区

P ⇌18 ◐🖐

TEL. 5386 5757

黄浦区淮海中路138号上海广场
5楼503号

**No. 503, 5F, Shanghai Plaza,
138 Middle Huaihai Road, Huangpu**

www.xinrongji.cc

■ 价钱 **PRICE**
午膳 Lunch
点菜 à la carte ￥ 200-300
晚膳 Dinner
点菜 à la carte ￥ 300-400

■ 营业时间 **OPENING HOURS**
午膳 Lunch 11:00-14:00 (L.O.)
晚膳 Dinner 17:00-21:00 (L.O.)

✿

新荣记（黄浦）

XIN RONG JI (HUANGPU)

中国菜·时尚

Chinese · Contemporary décor

一家位于商场内的中菜厅，地铁站就在对面，位置十
分便利。餐室内部环境充满浓烈中国色彩，入口处
的一列神像尤为引人注目。然而，吸引人的还有这儿
的美味佳肴，主角是台州海鲜，辅以一系列出色的粤
菜，午市还有广东点心供应。家烧黄鱼、炖汤和纸包
叉烧都是推介菜式。

A wall of statues by the entrance demonstrate
the effort that has gone into the decoration of
this Chinese restaurant, located in a shopping
mall opposite a metro station. However, the real
attraction is the food. Seafood from Taizhou is
the undoubted highlight, but the Cantonese
food and the dim sum are carefully prepared.
Look out for the sautéed yellow croaker and
BBQ pork in a paper bag.

甬府

YONG FU

宁波菜·古典

Ningbo · Historic

上海人对宁波菜准不会陌生，为满足挑咀的食客，煮出最传统和地道的风味，厨师由开业至今坚持选用产自宁波的食材，包括各种海产皆每天新鲜运抵。主餐室设有六张餐桌，另设九间连洗手间的私人厢房，是举行各种聚会的尚佳之选。

Shanghainese are no strangers to Ningbo cuisine and can be hard to please. This classy restaurant, with its old Shanghai glamour fares well with wild-caught seafood shipped daily from Ningbo, authentically prepared and artfully plated. The dining hall houses six tables while the nine private rooms with ensuites seat up to 18 guests each, all adorned by exquisite artwork and furnished with heavy wood chairs and tables.

P ⇔18 ◐⏹

TEL. 3356 6777

黄浦区茂名南路59号锦江饭店锦北楼12楼

12F, Cathay Building, Jin Jiang Hotel, 59 South Maoming Road, Huangpu

■ 价钱 **PRICE**

午膳 Lunch
点菜 à la carte ¥ 500-800
晚膳 Dinner
点菜 à la carte ¥ 700-1,000

■ 营业时间 **OPENING HOURS**

午膳 Lunch 11:00-13:45 (L.O.)
晚膳 Dinner 17:00-21:00 (L.O.)

TEL. 5306 6604
黄浦区思南路36号
36 Sinan Road, Huangpu

■ 价钱 PRICE
点菜 à la carte ¥ 20-50

■ 营业时间 OPENING HOURS
11:00-20:00 (L.O.)

阿娘面
A NIANG MIAN

面食 · 简朴
Noodles · Simple

店子外表平实无华，繁忙时段却常见长长的人龙在店外等候，明显食客都是冲着食物而来。这里提供十多款地道面食和数款浇头，其中黄鱼面和爆鳝面最为知名，伴以咸菜肉丝或素鸡等浇头，便能大快朵颐。小店采用半自助形式，顾客需先在门口柜枱点餐付费，然后找个位子坐下，服务员便会将餐点奉上。

If you arrive at this very popular noodle shop at peak time the first thing you'll notice is the queue. When you get to the front, place your order and pay at the counter at the entrance before finding a seat. The standouts are yellow croaker noodles, and noodles with stir-fried eels. To better experience the skills of the chef here, it's also worth ordering side dishes, such as shredded pork with pickled vegetables.

翡翠酒家（黄浦）
CRYSTAL JADE (HUANGPU)

粤菜·舒适

Cantonese · Cosy

新加坡翡翠集团在上海首家食店，现代装潢中带点中国风，倚窗而设的卡座最受欢迎，餐室中央一张长桌子可让客人拼桌。餐厅颇受上班一族欢迎，但晚上及假日亦不乏慕名而来的游客。叫食客光临的正是其正宗广东美食，其中点心由广东师傅主理，肠粉、虾饺等特别出色。作为新加坡集团，其黑白胡椒炒青蟹亦值得一试。假日宜预早订座。

The Singapore-based group's first restaurant in Shanghai features a strikingly modern interior – ask for one of the prized booths by the window. Many come for a business lunch on weekdays while quite a number of tourists are attracted at night and on weekends. Dim sum is meticulously made by Cantonese chefs – shrimp dumplings and rice noodle rolls are the highlights. Singaporean pepper crab is also worth a try. Booking essential at weekends.

P ⇔10 ℃🍴

TEL. 6385 8752

黄浦区兴业路123号新天地广场南里2楼12 A-B

12 A-B, 2F, South Block, Xintiandi, 123 Xingye Road, Huangpu

www.crystaljade.com

■ 价钱 PRICE
午膳 Lunch
点菜 à la carte ¥ 100-150
晚膳 Dinner
点菜 à la carte ¥ 180-250

■ 营业时间 OPENING HOURS
11:00-21:40 (L.O.)

黄浦区 HUANGPU

黄浦区四川中路136号
136 Middle Sichuan Road, Huangpu

■ 价钱 PRICE
午膳 Lunch
点菜 à la carte ¥ 8-20
晚膳 Dinner
点菜 à la carte ¥ 8-20

■ 营业时间 OPENING HOURS
06:30-19:00 (L.O.)

大壶春（四川中路）
DA HU CHUN
(MIDDLE SICHUAN ROAD)

点心 · 简朴

Dian Xin · Simple

这家老字号生煎包店早于1932年开业，以自助形式服务的店子面积不大，门外络绎不绝的食客正是慕现做的生煎包和小云吞之名而来。它们的包子并不如潮流的汤汁如泉涌，但包底香脆可口，馅料丰腴鲜美，叫人齿颊回香，刚上碟时品尝最佳。这里也供应蟹壳黄等点心，更设小卖部售卖各式上海糯米糕点和生云吞。

Queues stretch down the street thanks to the pan-fried pork buns which are cooked to perfection, with a crisp base and a juicy filling. Besides the buns, you can find mini wontons and Shaobing with a meat filling. The original shop opened here in 1932; it moved, subsequently returned to the same street, and now has several other shops scattered across Shanghai. You can also buy uncooked dim sum to take home and cook.

海金滋（黄浦）
HAI JIN ZI (HUANGPU)

沪菜·简朴
Shanghainese · Simple

进贤路近陕西路的转角处，可找到这家小小的店子，简单平实的餐室内放了数张桌子，虽然食客要挤拥着用膳，但为着那酱油色浓重的老派本帮菜，挤一点也是值得的。葱烤大排、酱鸭和糖醋小黄鱼都是厨师的拿手菜。浓油赤酱的传统滋味，配上一碗白饭，叫人满意饱足，回味无穷。

None of the customers seem to mind the congestion that comes with having just eight tables. They simply keep coming back to this modestly designed little shop for more of the traditional Shanghainese dishes, which are robustly seasoned and cooked to a caramel colour. Try the scallion pork chop; the braised duck; or the yellow croaker in sweet vinegar sauce – and don't forget to order a bowl of steamed rice to go with them.

TEL. 6255 0371
黄浦区进贤路240号
240 Jinxian Road, Huangpu

■ 价钱 PRICE
午膳 Lunch
点菜 à la carte ¥ 60-100
晚膳 Dinner
点菜 à la carte ¥ 60-100

■ 营业时间 OPENING HOURS
午膳 Lunch 11:00-14:00 (L.O.)
晚膳 Dinner 17:00-20:30 (L.O.)

黄浦区 HUANGPU

P ⇦16 ◐⧲

TEL. 3366 3777

黄浦区南京西路288号
创兴金融中心3楼

**3F, Chong Hing Finance Center,
288 West Nanjing Road, Huangpu**

www.jade388.com

■ **价钱 PRICE**
午膳 Lunch
点菜 à la carte ￥200-400
晚膳 Dinner
点菜 à la carte ￥200-500

■ **营业时间 OPENING HOURS**
11:00-22:45 (L.O.)

苏浙汇（南京西路）
JARDIN DE JADE
(WEST NANJING ROAD)

沪菜・时尚

Shanghainese ・ Contemporary décor

位于魔都的中央商业核心区，邻近人民公园，坐拥宜人园景，这家苏浙汇非常宽敞，装潢典雅时尚，感觉舒适。秉承品牌传统，菜单上的是较新派的上海菜，时令的精选食材、道地的口味、时尚的摆盘，让你品味不一样的沪菜。络绎不绝的食客令服务员有点应接不暇。

It's located in a shiny office block overlooking People's Park, so it's not altogether surprising to find the local business community flocking here at lunchtime – although this can lead to the service team becoming a little stretched. On offer at this big, stylish restaurant is a menu of Shanghainese dishes and, in particular, Jiangnan cuisine. Dishes are presented in a modern style and menus are supplemented by seasonal specials.

金刚馄饨还有面（蒙自路）
KING KONG DUMPLING & NOODLES (MENGZI ROAD)

面食 · 简朴
Noodles · Simple

这家现代装潢的面馆出品的馄饨和面食口味道地，受欢迎自有其独到之处，如高汤用上大量大骨熬制二十四个小时、葱油用上三种葱烹煮而成、黄鱼汤每天现熬等。最热卖的食品有菜肉馄饨、鸡骨酱面，你还可以添加自己喜欢的浇头。夏天时最好来一碗麻酱冷面。

This simple shop sets the bar for Shanghainese wontons and noodles. The chef prepares the broth with a vast amount of bones and it simmers for over 24 hours; the scallion oil uses three kinds of scallion; and the yellow croaker soup is freshly made each day. Try the pork and vegetable dumpling or the chicken bone noodle with your own choice of topping; in summer the cold sesame noodles are the way to go.

TEL. 6302 2836
黄浦区蒙自路207号11号楼001A
001A, Block 11, 207 Mengzi Road, Huangpu

■ 价钱 **PRICE**
午膳 Lunch
点菜 à la carte ¥ 20-50
晚膳 Dinner
点菜 à la carte ¥ 20-50

■ 营业时间 **OPENING HOURS**
午膳 Lunch 11:00-14:00 (L.O.)
晚膳 Dinner 17:30-02:30 (L.O.)

黄浦区 **HUANGPU**

黄浦区 HUANGPU

🍴 ⚥🍽

TEL. 5306 9650

黄浦区西藏中路180号高盛商厦1楼

**1F, Gaosheng Building,
180 Middle Xizang Road, Huangpu**

■ 价钱 **PRICE**
午膳 Lunch
点菜 à la carte ¥ 50-100
晚膳 Dinner
点菜 à la carte ¥ 50-100

■ 营业时间 **OPENING HOURS**
午膳 Lunch 11:00-14:00 (L.O.)
晚膳 Dinner 16:30-21:30 (L.O.)

■ 休息日期 **ANNUAL AND WEEKLY
CLOSING**
农历新年休息8天
Closed 8 days Lunar New Year

😀

兰亭

LAN TING

沪菜·亲切

Shanghainese · Neighbourhood

从嵩山路迁至西藏中路，新餐室灯火通明，面积增大了，可以招待更多客人，缩短轮候时间。食物素质仍保持一贯水准，厨师坚持以新鲜食材烹调家常菜，价钱亦依旧亲民。菜单跟以前变化不大，必点菜式包括用鸡腿肉烹煮的鸡骨酱，还有面拖黄鱼。由于新鲜食材存量有限，为免尝不到心仪菜式还是不要太晚抵埗。

It may have moved to a new location in 2018 but this Shanghainese restaurant still offers warm service, fresh ingredients and delicious home-style dishes. While the dining room is now brighter and bigger (shortening the waiting time significantly), the prices remain wallet-friendly. Must-try items include braised chicken in brown sauce and fried yellow croaker. Most ingredients are in limited supply and it's advisable to come early.

BE CURIOUS
马爹利 好奇于心

兰心
LAN XIN

沪菜·亲切

Shanghainese · Neighbourhood

说兰心是进贤路上人气最高的食店也一点也不过分，每次经过其门前，总会看到门外坐着等候座位的客人。原为旧民居的餐室，充满怀旧气息，与供应的老上海家常菜相对应：红烧肉、酱鸭、油爆虾和糖醋小黄鱼等，都是大家熟悉的本帮菜，每次去到兰心，总会禁不住再点这几道菜式，重温那滋味。

There's a plethora of places to eat on Jinxian Road but one worth searching out is little Lan Xin. It's a popular place with a diverse clientele – just be ready to join the queue, which usually snakes down the street. It was once a residential home and the modest look matches with the traditional, homely style of Shanghainese food on offer. The braised pork; braised duck with brown sauce; and yellow croaker in sweet vinegar sauce are all good.

TEL. 6253 3554

黄浦区进贤路130号
130 Jinxian Road, Huangpu

■ 价钱 **PRICE**
午膳 Lunch
点菜 à la carte ￥60-100
晚膳 Dinner
点菜 à la carte ￥60-100

■ 营业时间 **OPENING HOURS**
午膳 Lunch 11:00-13:30 (L.O.)
晚膳 Dinner 17:00-21:00 (L.O.)

黄浦区 **HUANGPU**

餐厅 RESTAURANTS

49

🍴20 🕐🍴

TEL. 6328 0602

黄浦区城隍庙豫园老街115号

**115 Yuyuan Old Street,
City God Temple, Huangpu**

■ 价钱 **PRICE**
午膳 Lunch
点菜 à la carte ¥ 150-300
晚膳 Dinner
点菜 à la carte ¥ 150-300

■ 营业时间 **OPENING HOURS**
午膳 Lunch 11:00-14:00 (L.O.)
晚膳 Dinner 17:00-20:30 (L.O.)

😋

绿波廊

LU BO LANG

沪菜・传统

Shanghainese・Traditional

城隍庙和豫园一带全是宝贵古迹，而绿波廊就在九曲桥旁依水而建的明朝旧建筑内，店内陈设也是充满中式韵味。在这里，你既可欣赏园林古建筑、又能品尝道地本帮菜肴。到绿波廊一定要尝尝那里的点心：萝卜丝饼、桂花拉糕、眉花酥等等全是招牌美食。餐厅预计在2019年初关闭装修。

Tourists and fans of heritage buildings seeking nourishment and some traditional Shanghainese food after visiting Yu Garden and walking the Bridge of Nine Turnings often find themselves at this characterful Chinese pavilion, built in the style of the Ming Dynasty. Dim sum is where the kitchen's strength lies, with turnip pastry, osmanthus flower pudding and 'eyebrow' cake some of the dishes to order. The restaurant will be closed for renovation in early 2019.

茂隆
MAO LONG

沪菜 · 亲切

Shanghainese · Neighbourhood

想品尝地道的本帮家常菜？进贤路上的茂隆是不错的选择。这儿有不少小餐厅，认着蓝色的门楣就不会走错。由民居改装而成的餐室面积小小却五脏俱全，内里放了五张桌子共二十个座位，繁忙时段要有拼桌的心理准备。餐单上渔鲜水产菜式选择丰富，可别忘了点选叫厨师引以为傲的红烧肉。

In among the plethora of simple eateries on Jinxian Road is this little place – just look out for the eye-catching blue sign. It was adapted from a residential property and as it has just 5 tables and around 20 seats you'll more than likely be sharing your table. Shanghainese home-style dishes are the draw; they offer numerous seafood choices but are particularly proud of their braised pork.

☐☐ ☒☐

TEL. 6256 1167
黄浦区进贤路134号
134 Jinxian Road, Huangpu

■ 价钱 PRICE
午膳 Lunch
点菜 à la carte ¥ 60-100
晚膳 Dinner
点菜 à la carte ¥ 60-100

■ 营业时间 OPENING HOURS
午膳 Lunch 11:00-14:15 (L.O.)
晚膳 Dinner 17:00-21:15 (L.O.)

黄浦区 **HUANGPU**

黄浦区 HUANGPU

P ⊖12 ⊘🍽

TEL. 6206 6177

黄浦区太仓路128号1楼

1F, 128 Taicang Road, Huangpu

■ 价钱 PRICE
午膳 Lunch
点菜 à la carte ¥ 100-250
晚膳 Dinner
点菜 à la carte ¥ 100-250

■ 营业时间 OPENING HOURS
午膳 Lunch 11:00-14:00 (L.O.)
晚膳 Dinner 17:00-21:00 (L.O.)

😋

荣小馆（黄浦）

RONG CUISINE (HUANGPU)

台州菜·时髦

Taizhou · Fashionable

荣小馆是新荣记旗下定位年轻客群的品牌，故即使货源相同，价格相对较大众化，并着重给予顾客更多空间。每天运抵的食材九成来自浙江，厨师拿手炮制东海海鲜，仅以矿泉水和生抽烹煮，以家烧或红烧方式带出海鲜原汁原味，此外浙江农家菜亦值得一试。配合餐厅选址，此店特设夜宵菜单，而订座仅限于包厢。

A spin-off of Xin Rong Ji, targeting a younger audience at a lower price range. Service may not be as formal and refined as its pricier sister, but is still pleasant and friendly. Both share the same sources of ingredients so freshness is guaranteed. On the menu, grilled fish, seafood and farm-style Zhejiang cooking dominate. Seasoning tends to be light to allow authentic flavours to come through. Reservations are accepted for private rooms only.

天都里
TANDOOR

印度菜 · 异国风情

Indian · Exotic décor

早于1992年，天都里已开始传出印度独有的香气。光线充沛的餐室以丝绸之路为设计主题，象征天与地的两色木砖上，缀有丝路沿途的地标建筑装饰。在此充满异国情调的餐厅，来自印度的团队带来北印度的传统滋味，除了咖喱和烧烤菜式，每天新鲜烤制的薄饼也是巧手之作。

Since 1992, it's been kind of an institution for Indian food in Shanghai. The décor has a Silk Road theme to it, with motifs taken from countries along the ancient trade route. Ample natural daylight and cosy seats complement the attentive service. All chefs are brought in from northern India for the most authentic cooking possible. Besides curries and BBQ, enjoy their naan freshly baked in the tandoor oven.

P ⇔8 ◐〒

TEL. 6472 5494

黄浦区茂名南路59号锦江饭店锦楠楼大堂

Lobby, Cathay Garden (South Building), Jin Jiang Hotel, 59 South Maoming Road, Huangpu

www.tandoorchina.cn

■ 价钱 PRICE
午膳 Lunch
套餐 set ¥ 88
点菜 à la carte ¥ 110-200
晚膳 Dinner
点菜 à la carte ¥ 200-300

■ 营业时间 OPENING HOURS
午膳 Lunch 11:30-14:00 (L.O.)
晚膳 Dinner 17:30-22:30 (L.O.)

黄浦区 HUANGPU

黄浦区 HUANGPU

♿15 🕐🍴

TEL. 6322 5266

黄浦区福建中路345号
345 Middle Fujian Road, Huangpu

■ 价钱 PRICE
午膳 Lunch
点菜 à la carte ¥ 100-200
晚膳 Dinner
点菜 à la carte ¥ 100-200

■ 营业时间 OPENING HOURS
午膳 Lunch 11:00-14:00 (L.O.)
晚膳 Dinner 17:00-21:00 (L.O.)

😊

扬州饭店（黄浦）
YANGZHOU FAN DIAN (HUANGPU)

淮扬菜・舒适

Huai Yang・Cosy

这家老字号饭店主理淮扬风味小菜，风味正宗、做工精细，收取的是平民价钱，因此深受上海人欢迎。福建中路的这家分店占地三层，2017年完成翻新后餐室缀以山水和动物画作，二楼更放有大型金色雕刻画，更添中式韵味，而玻璃窗外是繁盛市貌，蛮有趣味。推介菜式有扬州干丝、狮子头和拆烩千岛湖鱼头等。

This senior member of the Shanghai dining scene is as busy as ever, especially after a facelift in 2017 that added a private room. The dining room is now decorated with paintings and wood carvings, while the floor-to-ceiling window on the second floor still frames the gorgeous city views. As always, it serves authentic Huaiyang food, impeccably made and reasonably priced. Must-tries include shredded tofu in soup and braised pork balls.

54

ATTO PRIMO

意大利菜 · 舒适
Italian · Cosy

Atto Primo位于逾九十年历史的日清大楼，能一览浦东景色，置于柜台前的披萨烤炉为餐厅带来生气。来自西西里岛的主厨专注于烹调意大利菜，菜式风味正宗且卖相甚佳——小牛肉薄片的金枪鱼酱甚为美味；香煎火腿小牛肉三文尼娜团子则是主厨重新演绎的传统菜式；最后别忘了尝尝酿了幼滑奶酪的奶油甜馅煎饼卷。

In a historic building circa 1925 on the Bund with Pudong views, this Italian restaurant prides itself on the atmosphere enjoyed at its counter seats in front of a grill and pizza oven. The Sicilian owner chef feed diners the Italian way – with well-made, attractive food in generous portions. Highlights include vitello tonnato, saltimbocca alla Romana served with gnocchi, and cannolo Siciliano with ricotta cream and pistachio filling.

🍴 ♿20
TEL. 6328 0272
黄浦区广东路20号外滩5号2楼
2F, Bund 5, 20 Guangdong Road, Huangpu
www.attoprimo.com.cn

■ 价钱 PRICE
午膳 Lunch
点菜 à la carte ¥ 400-1,000
晚膳 Dinner
点菜 à la carte ¥ 400-1,000

■ 营业时间 OPENING HOURS
午膳 Lunch 11:30-14:30 (L.O.)
晚膳 Dinner 17:30-22:30 (L.O.)

黄浦区 HUANGPU

&. ⟲12 ◎🍴

TEL. 6330 8217

黄浦区南京东路139号
外滩中央5楼501室
**Room 501, 5F, The Bund Central,
139 East Nanjing Road, Huangpu**

■ 价钱 PRICE
午膳 Lunch
套餐 set ¥ 388-988
点菜 à la carte ¥ 100-250
晚膳 Dinner
套餐 set ¥ 388-988
点菜 à la carte ¥ 200-400

■ 营业时间 OPENING HOURS
午膳 Lunch 11:00-14:00 (L.O.)
晚膳 Dinner 17:30-21:30 (L.O.)

■ 休息日期 ANNUAL AND WEEKLY
CLOSING
农历新年5天及公众假期休息
Closed 5 days Lunar New Year and
Public Holidays

🍴○

喜粤8号（南京东路）ⓝ
CANTON 8 (EAST NANJING ROAD)

粤菜·亲密

Cantonese · Intimate

餐厅位处一幢建于三十年代并经改建的商场之内，内部装潢充满当时的英式风味。餐牌与汝南路总店有八成相同，但定位更为高档。琳琅满目的菜单上除了即场制作的点心、经六小时炖煮的炖汤，当然亦少不了海鲜菜式，包括每天进货的龙趸。而为保食材新鲜，多数海鲜须预订。餐厅只接受午间十一时半前及晚间六时前的订位。

The décor befits the heritage of the circa 1930 architecture in the former British Concession. The menu is mostly the same as the Runan Street flagship, but this branch focuses on high-end dishes, such as fried scallops in mashed taro and giant grouper which is shipped in daily. Dim sum is made in-house and soups are double-boiled for at least six hours. Only reservations before 6pm for dinner and 11:30am for lunch are accepted.

恰
CHAR

扒房·时尚
Steakhouse · Contemporary décor

位于酒店高层，开扬的景观、偌大的餐室搭配充满乡村风味的设计：舒适的扶手椅、柔和的灯光，加上深棕色乡土风格的木板天花，浪漫的情调伴随着轻松的氛围，用餐成了难以言喻的美妙体验！冷肉选择丰富兼具品质，如来自澳洲的获奖和牛等是菜单的一大特点。店内的酒吧是用餐前后的最佳休憩处。

Great views are a given as this large steakhouse is located on the top floor of the Indigo hotel. It's also a warm and intimate space, thanks to the rustic wooden ceiling and the big, comfortable armchairs. The menu offers a large choice of meats, with the highlight being the Blackmore Wagyu from Australia. The Char Bar is an equally pleasant spot for a drink before or after dinner.

TEL. 3302 9995
黄浦区中山东二路585号
外滩英迪格酒店29-31楼

29-31F, Indigo Hotel,
585 Zhongshan Dong Er Road,
Huangpu
www.char-thebund.com

■ 价钱 PRICE
晚膳 Dinner
套餐 set ￥798-1,398
点菜 à la carte ￥750-3,940

■ 营业时间 OPENING HOURS
晚膳 Dinner 17:30-22:30 (L.O.)

黄浦区 HUANGPU

🔧14 🍴

TEL. 6321 2010

黄浦区九江路216号
216 Jiujiang Road, Huangpu

■ 价钱 PRICE
午膳 Lunch
点菜 à la carte ¥ 300-500
晚膳 Dinner
点菜 à la carte ¥ 400-1,000

■ 营业时间 OPENING HOURS
11:00-22:00 (L.O.)

🍴

成隆行蟹王府（黄浦）
CHENG LONG HANG (HUANGPU)

沪菜・东方

Shanghainese • Oriental décor

爱吃大闸蟹者对此专门店不会陌生，其自设的大型养殖场确保货源优质，在其他时节亦供应各式大闸蟹菜式，秃黄油捞饭和清炒蟹粉均是必尝之选，前者以母蟹之黄加上公蟹之膏煮成，丰腴美味，后者耗用三十多只蟹而成，叫人再三回味。店内装潢别致，一如明清徽式风格的小戏台，每晚更设丝竹表演。

Crabs from its own farm are used at this famous hairy crab restaurant. It also serves assorted dishes made with hairy crab – try the crab roe rice which uses a mixture of both male and female crabs; stir-fried crab roes, a dish which can use up to 30 crabs; and other premium seafood. The restaurant is decorated in the style of ancient Huizhou and every night you can enjoy Sizhu, a musical recital.

壳里

COQUILLE

法国菜·时尚

French · Contemporary décor

占地两层的壳里以金属元素和黑白纹格地砖营造出悠闲的情调和精致的環境，二楼用餐区相对私密，适合小型聚会。它与比邻的意大利餐厅Scarpetta由同一单位主理，不同的是这儿以法国菜为主打，在传统菜肴中揉合了东南亚元素。焦糖鹅肝布丁和秘制香烤珍宝蟹是厨师得意之作，餐牌上没有显示的威灵顿牛肉更是必试之选，建议提早预订。

Next to the Italian trattoria Scarpetta you'll find its younger sibling Coquille, a charming French restaurant with brass and mosaics. It's spread over two floors, with the upstairs room providing a little more intimacy. The French classics come with subtle Southeast Asian influences. Signature dishes include foie gras crème brûlée and oven-roasted Dungeness crab. Pre-ordering beef Wellington is a must.

P ⓒ🍴
TEL. 3376 8127
黄浦区蒙自路29号
29 Mengzi Road, Huangpu
www.coquille.com.cn

■ 价钱 PRICE
晚膳 Dinner
点菜 à la carte ¥ 500-1,000

■ 营业时间 OPENING HOURS
晚膳 Dinner 17:30-21:30 (L.O.)

■ 休息日期 ANNUAL AND WEEKLY CLOSING
农历新年休息7天
Closed 7 days Lunar New Year

黄浦区 HUANGPU

TEL. 5383 2031

黄浦区广东路20号外滩5号6楼
6F, Bund 5, 20 Guangdong Road,
Huangpu

■ 价钱 PRICE
午膳 Lunch
点菜 à la carte ¥ 300-700
晚膳 Dinner
点菜 à la carte ¥ 300-700

■ 营业时间 OPENING HOURS
周末午膳 Weekend lunch
11:30-14:30 (L.O.)
晚膳 Dinner 17:00-22:00 (L.O.)

■ 休息日期 ANNUAL AND WEEKLY
CLOSING
农历新年休息4天
Closed 4 days Lunar New Year

厨魔馆

DAIMON GASTROLOUNGE

时尚中国菜·前卫

Chinese contemporary · Trendy

混凝土地板、金属支架和涂鸦营造出独特的环境，服
务员的装扮也叫人惊喜——有穿着旧香港警察制服
的、中国功夫服饰的、李小龙戏服的。相比之下，食
物就不那么怀旧和叫人眼熟，相反是巧用西式食材的
创意中菜。若眼前一切冲击太大，不妨欣赏一下窗外
华美的黄浦江景色。

Inspired by Kowloon Walled City and
loaded with graffiti and loud music, Daimon
Gastrolounge is a casual joint that is wild and
untamed in both its décor and food. Even
servers dress the part from Hong Kong pop
culture circa 1960s. The menu features typical
Alvin Leung's tricks – modern Cantonese fare
juxtaposed with Western food to challenge
your expectations. Try Peking duck confit. The
view of the Bund is also a plus.

HUANGPU 黄浦区

德兴馆（广东路）
DE XING GUAN (GUANGDONG ROAD)

沪菜·亲切

Shanghainese · Neighbourhood

创于1878年，广东路上的总店有着夺目的金漆招牌和中式楼阁门面，地面层是售卖面食和盖浇饭的面馆，沿着楼梯回旋而上，则是环境较舒适的餐室和包厢，供应本帮上海菜，冷盘、热菜、汤品和面食点心等一应俱全。其面食和点心都是店内鲜制，厨师们每天清晨四点就到来准备，尤其推介两鲜面和三鲜面。

Founded in 1878, this two-storey noodle shop is something of a local landmark thanks to its gilded sign and elaborate façade. Chefs start work at 4am, making noodles and dim sum from scratch. The ground floor serves 20 different noodle and rice dishes, including the famous three-treasure soup noodles (fried eel, fried fish and pork hock). The dining room upstairs offers more comfort and a bigger Shanghainese menu, from soups to hot dishes and dim sum.

🪑20

TEL. 6352 2535

黄浦区广东路471号
471 Guangdong Road, Huangpu

■ 价钱 **PRICE**
午膳 Lunch
点菜 à la carte ¥ 20-80
晚膳 Dinner
点菜 à la carte ¥ 50-100

■ 营业时间 **OPENING HOURS**
午膳 Lunch 11:00-13:45 (L.O.)
晚膳 Dinner 17:00-20:45 (L.O.)

黄浦区 **HUANGPU**

📺 🚫🍷

TEL. 5107 9177

黄浦区淮海中路494弄22号
22 Lane, 494 Middle Huaihai Road, Huangpu

■ 价钱 **PRICE**
午膳 Lunch
点菜 à la carte ¥ 10-30

■ 营业时间 **OPENING HOURS**
24小時 24 hours

🍴

顶特勒粥面馆
DING TE LE ZHOU MIAN GUAN

粥面·简朴
Noodles and Congee · Simple

这家粥面馆藏身于淮海路雁荡路对面的一条弄堂里，简朴的店面与一般上海弄堂食店大相迳庭，不甚显眼，走近店门，粥、面、饭和小食的香气却扑鼻而来。店子所售的地道面食甚受欢迎，葱油肉丝面、雪菜黄鱼面和香炸大排更是热卖之选。店家廿四小时营业，食客可到阁楼的小餐室享用。

To the passer-by, this simple shop hidden in an alley on Huaihai Road looks pretty much like any other. What sets it apart, however, are the authentic noodles it serves. It is particularly famous for its shredded pork noodles with scallions, its yellow croaker noodles with pickled vegetables, and its deep-fried pork chops. You can also enjoy congee, rice and snacks – and it stays open 24 hours a day.

鼎苑

DING YUAN

沪菜 · 舒适

Shanghainese · Cosy

依码头而立，窗外是摩登浮华的黄浦江景色，餐厅内十五个豪华包厢风格各异，由艺术家所绘的画作高挂，甚为雅致，部分更设独立洗手间，私隐度高。与环境相呼应的是其食物，厨师讲究用料，例如招牌烤鸭选用从北京空运而到的鸭子，客人更可透过玻璃观赏烧烤过程。设最低消费，建议预早订座。

Nestled by the picturesque Huangpu River, its made-to-order menu is served in its 15 private rooms, seating up to 18 guests each. The décor blends old Shanghai with modernism and features oil paintings by famous artists. Its signature Peking duck is shipped from Beijing and diners can watch it being roasted in the kitchen behind the glass. Dim sum is served at lunch. Minimum charge applies. Early reservations are recommended.

TEL. 5308 8526

黄浦区外马路601号3号库3楼301号

**Room 301, 3F, Block 3,
601 Waima Road, Huangpu**

■ 价钱 PRICE
午膳 Lunch
点菜 à la carte ¥ 600-800
晚膳 Dinner
点菜 à la carte ¥ 600-800

■ 营业时间 OPENING HOURS
午膳 Lunch 11:00-14:00 (L.O.)
晚膳 Dinner 17:00-21:00 (L.O.)

黄浦区 HUANGPU

🪑 ⛓40 ⛓🍴

TEL. 5169 0989

黄浦区汉口路309号
309 Hankou Road, Huangpu

■ 价钱 PRICE
午膳 Lunch
套餐 set ¥ 128-158
点菜 à la carte ¥ 320-520
晚膳 Dinner
点菜 à la carte ¥ 320-520

■ 营业时间 OPENING HOURS
11:30-21:45 (L.O.)

🍴○🍴

香料与鹅肝

ÉPICES & FOIE GRAS

时尚法国菜·型格

French contemporary · Design

与繁忙的南京东路隔了两座大厦，坐落于较为宁静的
地段，穿过小小的入口，便是这家空间不大、设计时
尚而不落俗套、感觉舒适轻松的法国小酒馆。年轻的
法裔夫妇，以多种不同烹调方式处理鹅肝，致力让食
客尝到与别不同的滋味。鹅肝三部曲和开心果百里煎
羊排是招牌菜。

It's no great surprise that foie gras is
the speciality here. It comes in different
preparations, so try the 'Trilogy' if you want
to sample various types. This 'modern French
bistrot' is run by a young French couple and
they wisely also serve other classic Gallic
dishes, like roasted lamb rack with crispy
Iranian pistachio and a light garlic infused
cream sauce. Like its façade, the main
dining room is somewhat diminutive but it is
pleasantly decorated.

GINZA ONODERA

日本菜・舒适

Japanese • Cosy

餐厅由三个部分组成：寿司房、铁板烧房和天妇罗房。寿司房由曾于香港分店工作两年的厨师担任主厨，与一般寿司店不同，这儿以红醋米作寿司饭。店内的鲑鱼籽和海胆来自北海道，厨师会以秘方腌制鲑鱼籽。招牌菜包括白金和牛铁板烧和海胆天妇罗。

This Japanese restaurant is divided into three sections, each serving a different style of food – sushi, teppanyaki and tempura – and each one led by its own Japanese chef. At the handsome sushi counter you'll find red vinegar being used with the rice. The salmon roe, marinated using the chef's secret recipe, and the sea urchin from Hokkaido are well worth trying.

🍴 ♿15 � ⏰ 🅿

TEL. 6333 9818

黄浦区中山东一路18号外滩18号
3楼303铺

Shop 303, 3F, Bund 18,
18 Zhongshan Dong Yi Road,
Huangpu

www.leoc-j.com

■ 价钱 **PRICE**

午膳 Lunch
套餐 set ￥ 228-980
点菜 à la carte ￥ 600-1,500
晚膳 Dinner
套餐 set ￥ 780-2,180
点菜 à la carte ￥ 600-1,500

■ 营业时间 **OPENING HOURS**
午膳 Lunch 11:30-13:00 (L.O.)
晚膳 Dinner 17:30-23:00 (L.O.)

■ 休息日期 **ANNUAL AND WEEKLY CLOSING**
农历新年休息3天
Closed 3 days Lunar New Year

 ⟨ 🖐 **P** ⟳36 ◻️ 🔔

TEL. 6321 5888

黄浦区中山东一路18号
外滩18号5楼

**5F, Bund 18,
18 Zhongshan Dong Yi Road,
Huangpu**

www.hakkasan.com

■ 价钱 **PRICE**
周五至周日早午拼餐 Friday to
Sunday brunch
套餐 set ￥298
点菜 à la carte ￥150-300
晚膳 Dinner
点菜 à la carte ￥600-800

■ 营业时间 **OPENING HOURS**
周五至周日早午拼餐 Friday to
Sunday brunch 11:00-14:30 (L.O.)
晚膳 Dinner 17:30-23:00 (L.O.)
周五及周六晚膳 Friday and Saturday
dinner 17:30-00:00 (L.O.)

🍴

HAKKASAN

中国菜 · 典雅

Chinese · Elegant

深沈的颜色搭配鲜红的吊灯、雕工精细的木饰和高级
家具，构造出独特、高贵的餐室风格。食物由集团内
经验丰富的厨师预备，黑松露和牛沙拉和香槟汁焗黑
鳕鱼是招牌菜。不妨邀请侍酒师为你从优秀的酒单中
选酒佐餐，品味最佳的酒菜组合。

The original Hakkasan opened in London in
2001 – now this international group stretches
all the way to the Bund. The Ling Ling Lounge,
the lattice woodwork and the dark colours help
create a glamorous and glitzy atmosphere.
The Cantonese cuisine is prepared with
considerable care by an experienced kitchen;
the salad of Australian Wagyu tenderloin with
black truffle, and the roasted silver cod with
champagne for two are the standouts.

黄浦区 HUANGPU

苏浙汇（淮海中路）

JARDIN DE JADE
(MIDDLE HUAIHAI ROAD)

沪菜·时尚

Shanghainese · Contemporary décor

此家苏浙汇是集团旗下十六家食店之一，供应现代风格的上海菜。个别菜式可以拼凑成一碟小菜，名为星盆，每碟星盆最多只能包含四款菜式。招牌菜清蒸鲥鱼是必定要尝试的菜式，每条鱼可供十人享用。以球形灯饰、水晶吊灯和典雅装饰的餐室，予人时尚感觉。

Most foodies in Shanghai will be familiar with Jardin de Jade as there are 16 branches around the city. Those who've never visited one can expect a menu of updated Shanghainese dishes. The speciality is Reeves shad – one fish can feed up to 10 people – but the menu has been cleverly designed so that one-person portions of certain dishes can also be ordered, so that you can mix and match with others in your group.

TEL. 6390 8989
黄浦区淮海中路283号
香港广场南座3楼05-08铺
Shop 05-08, 3F, Hong Kong Plaza
South Block, 283 Middle Huaihai
Road, Huangpu
www.jade388.com

■ 价钱 PRICE
午膳 Lunch
套餐 set ¥ 68
点菜 à la carte ¥ 180-300
晚膳 Dinner
点菜 à la carte ¥ 180-300

■ 营业时间 OPENING HOURS
11:00-22:45 (L.O.)

黄浦区 HUANGPU

🦐 ⏶12 ⚙ ⓘ🍴

TEL. 6340 0767

黄浦区广东路20号外滩5号5楼
**5F, Bund 5, 20 Guangdong Road,
Huangpu**

■ 价钱 **PRICE**
午膳 Lunch
套餐 set ¥ 200-280
点菜 à la carte ¥ 400-600
晚膳 Dinner
点菜 à la carte ¥ 400-600

■ 营业时间 **OPENING HOURS**
午膳 Lunch 11:30-14:30 (L.O.)
晚膳 Dinner 17:00-22:00 (L.O.)

■ 休息日期 **ANNUAL AND WEEKLY
CLOSING**
农历新年除夕休息1天
Closed 1 day Lunar New Year Eve

🍴⚪

老干杯
KANPAI CLASSIC

烧烤・时尚

Barbecue · Contemporary décor

这家和牛烤肉店由台湾干杯集团开设,供应十四种不同部位的顶级澳洲和牛,还有各种肉类、海产及各式和风食物。所用和牛皆由本地牧场直送并于店内熟成,确保素质。餐室风格时尚,每张桌子均配备燃碳烧炉,店员随时从旁协助。与亲朋好友边品尝肉汁淋漓的烤肉,边呷一口餐厅出品的清酒,实是一大享受。

If anything demonstrates the international nature of restaurants it's this: a Shanghai restaurant from a Taiwanese group, specialising in Australian Wagyu beef that also serves Japanese dishes. There are 14 cuts of premium Australian Wagyu, along with other meats and seafood, and each table has its own charcoal stove. The inexperienced shouldn't be afraid of asking the staff for assistance. The house-brand sake makes a great accompaniment.

逸荟
LA SOCIÉTÉ

粤菜 · 典雅
Cantonese · Elegant

圆明园路上的旧建筑群中开了许多餐厅，逸荟置身于女青年会大楼中，小小的电梯将你带到八楼，这儿全是包厢，上一层便是主餐室，举目尽是黑白二色的大理石，整个空间装饰得华贵而优雅。端上桌的粤菜也如室内的装潢般高贵，由点心、烧味、海鲜、海味以至于甜品，都做得细致而风味正宗，看得到店方的心思。

There are a vast number of dining options on Yuanmingyuan Road but if you're after elegantly presented and carefully prepared traditional Cantonese food then this is where to come. The tiny elevator brings you to the 8th floor where the private rooms are located – the main dining room is one level up. The highly experienced team behind this restaurant have put as much attention into the decoration as they have the cooking.

🛋 ⇔ 20 ☺🍴
TEL. 6323 6767

黄浦区圆明园路133号洛克·外滩源
女青年会大楼8-9楼
8-9F, Y.W.C.A. Building, Rockbund,
133 Yuanmingyuan Road, Huangpu

■ 价钱 **PRICE**
午膳 Lunch
点菜 à la carte ¥ 400-600
晚膳 Dinner
点菜 à la carte ¥ 600-800

■ 营业时间 **OPENING HOURS**
午膳 Lunch 11:30-14:30 (L.O.)
晚膳 Dinner 17:30-21:30 (L.O.)

黄浦区 **HUANGPU**

HUANGPU 黄浦区

🏠 P ⇄18 ⚙

TEL. 6426 0938

黄浦区思南路59号

59 Sinan Road, Huangpu

www.xiaonanguo.com/html/
brands_maison.php

■ 价钱 PRICE

午膳 Lunch
套餐 set ¥ 498-1,298
点菜 à la carte ¥ 200-400
晚膳 Dinner
套餐 set ¥ 498-1,298
点菜 à la carte ¥ 500-800

■ 营业时间 OPENING HOURS

午膳 Lunch 11:00-14:00 (L.O.)
晚膳 Dinner 17:30-21:30 (L.O.)

🍴

慧公馆（思南路）

MAISON DE L'HUI (SINAN ROAD)

中国菜·时髦

Chinese · Fashionable

餐厅开设在兴建于1920年代、环境清幽宜人的思南公馆内，建筑物内外都保留了法租界时期的特色，细小的房间内揉合了殖民时代的氛围与现代色彩的摆设，令你生出身处老上海的浮华世界中的暇想。主厨在烹饪界打滚多年，中菜如炖海螺汤和雪花牛肉等均造得很出色，不要错过。

Sinan Mansions provide a quiet retreat from the bustle of the city and here you'll find this Chinese restaurant. Divided into several small dining rooms, it mixes colourful, contemporary furniture with pieces inspired by 18th century French style. Standouts on the menu include the double-boiled sea whelk soup and the stone-grilled superior snowflake beef. The peaceful terrace is a lovely spot on which to enjoy the food.

MERCATO

意大利菜・时尚

Italian • Contemporary décor

和一般意大利餐厅不同，生气勃勃、充满活力的 Mercato 渗透着丝丝地中海风。木炭烤披萨如黑松露三种芝士和有机鸡蛋很受欢迎。其他招牌菜有龙虾和虾仁饺子、木炭烤整条冰岛比目鱼和酥脆牛肋排炸玉米条等都值得试试。数量和种类繁多的酒单上供应的大多数是来自意大利的佳酿。

From Jean-Georges Vongerichten comes this lively Italian restaurant with some Mediterranean twists. The self-styled "farm chic" décor means lots of natural materials juxtaposed with a certain urban savviness. Signature dishes include lobster and shrimp ravioli with lemon and herbs, and beef short ribs with polenta fries. The wood-fired oven is used to good effect, whether that's for a whole halibut or for pizzas like black truffle and cheese.

TEL. 6321 9922

黄浦区中山东一路3号外滩3号6楼

6F, Bund 3,
3 Zhongshan Dong Yi Road, Huangpu
www.threeonthebund.com

■ 价钱 PRICE
晚膳 Dinner
点菜 à la carte ¥ 260-600

■ 营业时间 OPENING HOURS
晚膳 Dinner 17:30-23:00 (L.O.)

黄浦区 HUANGPU

TEL. 6323 9898

黄浦区中山东一路18号外滩18号
6楼

**6F, Bund 18,
18 Zhongshan Dong Yi Road,
Huangpu**

www.mmbund.com

■ 价钱 **PRICE**
周末早午拼餐 Weekend brunch
套餐 set ¥ 250
晚膳 Dinner
套餐 set ¥ 488-1,388
点菜 à la carte ¥ 400-600

■ 营业时间 **OPENING HOURS**
周末早午拼餐 Weekend brunch
11:30-14:30 (L.O.)
晚膳 Dinner 17:30-22:30 (L.O.)
周四至周六晚膳 Thursday to
Saturday dinner 17:30-02:00 (L.O.)

MR & MRS BUND

时尚法国菜 · 时髦

French contemporary · Fashionable

长长的菜单内提供逾一百五十道挟着亚洲风味的法国菜，花多眼乱而选择困难？就尝尝主题式套餐吧！当然，你亦可以毫不犹豫地挑选其招牌菜如野餐鸡肉佐蒜泥蛋黄酱、黑松露面包、酱烧牛肋排和袋蒸黑鳕鱼。周末有早午拼餐和夜宵套餐供应。

A great soundtrack, a terrific wine list and bags of French joie de vivre make dining here quite an experience. Chef Paul Pairet's large restaurant is located in a former bank dating from 1922. Furniture inspired by 18th century France combines with lots of contemporary touches to create a striking room. The à la carte offers a vast choice of creative dishes which have their roots in France but come with Asian twists and global influences.

DON'T LEAVE HOME WITHOUT IT!

巅峰 "食" 刻与你相约
美国运通邀你尊享盛宴

找优惠，关注"美国运通"
www.americanexpress.com.cn

NAPA

时尚欧陆菜 · 时尚

European contemporary · Contemporary décor

室内装潢现代，与其身处的历史建筑相映成趣。入口展示的酒瓶和超过八百种名酿的酒单道出东主的背景，原是酒商的他于2007年开设酒吧，后转型为餐厅。餐单设三款套餐，单点菜式选择亦不俗。如欲以黄浦江美景搭配美酒用膳，便要尽早抵埗，因窗畔五张餐桌是先到先得的。

A dimly lit bar and restaurant in a heritage building on the Bund, NAPA serves contemporary European food meant to be enjoyed with wine. Three set menus (one aptly-named Introduction and another Gourmet) and the à la carte menu change seasonally and are well complemented by over 800 wines from all over the world, including some rare vintages. Arrive early for the tables overlooking the Huangpu river.

🚭 16

TEL. 6318 0057

黄浦区中山东二路22号
外滩22号2楼

**2F, Bund 22,
22 Zhongshan Dong Er Road,
Huangpu**

www.napawinebarandkitchen.com

■ 价钱 **PRICE**
晚膳 Dinner
套餐 set ￥438-1,068
点菜 à la carte ￥500-800

■ 营业时间 **OPENING HOURS**
晚膳 Dinner 18:00-22:30 (L.O.)

黄浦区 HUANGPU

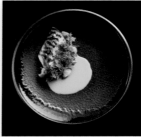

HUANGPU 黄浦区

🏠 ⬭12

TEL. 6080 2918

黄浦区毛家园路1-3号
上海南外滩水舍1楼

**1F, The Waterhouse at South Bund,
1-3 Maojiayuan Road, Huangpu**

www.oxalis-shanghai.com

■ 价钱 **PRICE**
午膳 Lunch
套餐 set ¥ 188
点菜 à la carte ¥ 270-440
晚膳 Dinner
点菜 à la carte ¥ 270-440

■ 营业时间 **OPENING HOURS**
午膳 Lunch 12:00-14:30 (L.O.)
晚膳 Dinner 18:00-22:00 (L.O.)

🍴🍽

欧社 Ⓝ

OXALIS

时尚欧陆菜・时尚

European contemporary・Contemporary décor

满有野心的主厨希望以相宜价钱呈献其学厨之路所习得的手艺。昏黄的灯光,配以当代手制陶瓷品,加上混凝土柱子和漆面木餐桌拼凑出工业风格的餐室;食客亦可选择在高台倚窗而坐,欣赏窗外景致。菜单上有不同分量的菜式,单独用膳或多人共聚也不乏选择。零度鸡肉冻糕、比目鱼佐豌豆及奶油蛋白饼都值得一试。

This loft-style restaurant in a developing hub near the south Bund waterfront has an industrial feel, with concrete pillars, iron flooring and reclaimed wood tables. The ambitious chef advocates 'bistronomy' – gastronomic food in a bistro setting at affordable prices. Specialities such as free-range chicken terrine, hazelnut-crusted halibut and Pavlova are all tasty and nicely presented. Order half portions to sample more variety.

PARIS ROUGE

法国菜·经典

French · Classic

静静地立于半岛酒店背后的一条狭小而隐蔽的街道上，是这家以红为主题、充满魅力的法国传统啤酒馆布置的菜馆。食物风味传统道地，千万别错过pâté en croute，其他食物如威灵顿牛肉及柠檬挞等也值得试试。喜欢呼吸新鲜空气的，可选择宁静的小阳台上的座位。餐厅将于2019年短暂关闭装修。

You'll find this little bit of Paris hidden down a narrow street behind The Peninsula hotel. Mirrors, black and white prints, bubble lamps and splashes of red help create that classic brasserie look, as do the waiters in their white aprons – it's an appealing spot, especially in the evening. Traditional dishes are to the fore, with the pâté en croute being a must-try, along with the beef Wellington and the lemon tart.

TEL. 5386 6011

黄浦区圆明园路133号
女青年会大楼102铺

**Shop 102, Y.W.C.A Building,
133 Yuanmingyuan Road, Huangpu**

■ 价钱 **PRICE**

午膳 Lunch
套餐 set ￥218-658
点菜 à la carte ￥250-380
晚膳 Dinner
套餐 set ￥398-658
点菜 à la carte ￥400-750

■ 营业时间 **OPENING HOURS**

午膳 Lunch 11:30-14:00 (L.O.)
晚膳 Dinner 18:00-21:30 (L.O.)

黄浦区 HUANGPU

黄浦区 HUANGPU

 ♿ 🅿️ ↺16 🍴🍽️ 🍴

TEL. 6322 9988

黄浦区中山东一路2号
外滩华尔道夫酒店大堂层

**Lobby Level, Waldorf Astoria Hotel,
2 Zhongshan Dong Yi Road, Huangpu**

www.waldorfastoriashanghai.com

■ 价钱 **PRICE**
晚膳 Dinner
套餐 set ￥600-1,200
点菜 à la carte ￥500-1,200

■ 营业时间 **OPENING HOURS**
晚膳 Dinner 17:30-22:00 (L.O.)

■ 休息日期 **ANNUAL AND WEEKLY
CLOSING**
七夕及平安夜休息1天
Closed Chinese Valentine's Day and
Christmas Eve

🍴🔘

PELHAM'S

时尚法国菜·经典

French contemporary · Classic

在华尔道夫酒店内的Pelham's，前身是曾为英国侨民
俱乐部的上海总会，店名实为该会创办人的名字，是
上海有名的高级餐厅，店内主要供应精致细腻的时尚
法国菜。庄严的设计风格，保守却感觉舒服。倒是大
幅玻璃墙能让食客观看部分厨房活动，大概这才是设
计者的心思所在。

The eponymous Sir Warren Pelham created
his Gentlemen's Club on this site in 1910 and
its wonderful main hall now plays host to this
comfortable and formal restaurant. Its rug-
covered wooden floors add to the atmosphere,
while the glass walls allow glimpses into the
kitchen. The modern, sophisticated cuisine has
a French base with a modern touch.

POP

美国菜 · 时尚
American · Contemporary décor

位于黄浦江畔建于1916年的外滩三号顶层，Pop坐拥最动人心魄的江畔景色。集时尚、古典与休闲于一身的室内设计，令你感到舒适自在，天台阳台上的座位是最佳的观景台。纽约客牛排、百利甜酒咖啡冰淇淋核桃挞、奶酪蛋糕草莓酸奶冰淇淋等充满浓浓的纽约风。

They've nailed that modern brasserie look but the best tables are those on the rooftop terrace, where you can take in views of the river and the skyscrapers. The cuisine is a comforting mix of American classics and some French influences. From New England chowder to Caesar salad, and New York strip steak to pecan pie, there is plenty on offer which will appeal. Start your evening with a drink on the bar terrace.

TEL. 6321 0909
黄浦区中山东一路3号外滩3号7楼
7F, Bund 3,
3 Zhongshan Dong Yi Road, Huangpu
www.threeonthebund.com

■ 价钱 **PRICE**
午膳 Lunch
套餐 set ¥ 178-298
点菜 à la carte ¥ 300-700
晚膳 Dinner
套餐 set ¥ 298-488
点菜 à la carte ¥ 300-700

■ 营业时间 **OPENING HOURS**
11:00-23:00 (L.O.)

黄浦区 HUANGPU

P ⇔20 🍴

TEL. 6335 1888

黄浦区河南中路88号
威斯汀大饭店2楼

**2F, The Westin Bund Center,
88 Middle Henan Road, Huangpu**

www.westin.com/shanghai

■ 价钱 **PRICE**
午膳 Lunch
套餐 set ¥ 168-298
点菜 à la carte ¥ 200-600
晚膳 Dinner
点菜 à la carte ¥ 200-600

■ 营业时间 **OPENING HOURS**
午膳 Lunch 11:30-14:00 (L.O.)
晚膳 Dinner 18:00-22:00 (L.O.)

🍴

帕戈

PREGO

意大利菜・亮丽

Italian・Colourful

色彩缤纷的环境，最适合与亲朋好友畅聚，品尝传统
意大利风味。意籍大厨热爱烹饪，亦爱与客人互动，
用膳时仿如在家般亲切。餐厅从世界各地搜罗优质食
材，菜单中包括厨师承传自母亲的鲜制意粉和提拉米
苏，不容错过的手制披萨经过24小时发酵后再以苹
果木烤烘而成，甜品车和手制意式冰淇淋叫人期待。

This bustling restaurant serving classic Italian
food has a relaxed, homely feel. The Salerno-
born chef pairs his family recipes with quality
ingredients shipped from all over the world,
including lobsters and wagyu beef. Pizzas
made with dough fermented for 24 hours are
baked in the apple wood-fired oven. Make sure
you save some room for homemade gelato or
something from the dessert trolley.

游宴一品淮扬

RIVER DRUNK

淮扬菜·豪华

Huai Yang · Luxury

餐室以晶莹玉石搭配翠绿琉璃，高雅中不失豪华气派，相得益彰是其供应的精致淮扬菜和粤菜。来自杭州的主厨喜以特别食材入馔，例如特色菜甬味鱼鲞合蒸，选用剖开晾干的鱼干制作；而海鲜冻米菜泡饭则在寻常海鲜泡饭中加入冻米，层次更为丰富。进餐同时不妨素描四周艺术画的二维条码，细味个中故事。

A recurring motif of white Yulan, the city flower of Shanghai, is part of the lavish decoration here, along with opulent materials such as glass and jade. The menu, as its name suggests, is geared slightly towards river fish lovers, with dishes such as steamed dried river fish Ningbo-style, puffed rice in seafood soup with leafy greens, and Xihu pastry with Zha Cai filling. Each private room is named after a flower, with matching themed cutlery.

 ♿ P ⌂25 ◐

TEL. 5368 8854

黄浦区中山东二路538号
万达瑞华酒店5楼

**5F, Wanda Reign Hotel,
538 Zhongshan Dong Er Road,
Huangpu**

www.wandahotels.com

■ 价钱 **PRICE**
套餐 set ¥130
点菜 à la carte ¥200-600
晚膳 Dinner
点菜 à la carte ¥400-700

■ 营业时间 **OPENING HOURS**
午膳 Lunch 11:30-14:30 (L.O.)
晚膳 Dinner 17:30-22:00 (L.O.)

黄浦区 HUANGPU

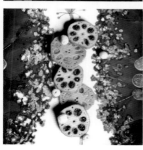

🖐 ⟳14 🍴
TEL. 6333 2981
黄浦区广东路20号外滩5号3楼
3F, Bund 5, 20 Guangdong Road, Huangpu
www.royalchinagroup.com

■ 价钱 **PRICE**
午膳 Lunch
点菜 à la carte ¥ 200-300
晚膳 Dinner
点菜 à la carte ¥ 400-500

■ 营业时间 **OPENING HOURS**
午膳 Lunch 11:00-14:30 (L.O.)
晚膳 Dinner 17:00-21:30 (L.O.)

黄浦区 HUANGPU

🍴

皇朝会
ROYAL CHINA CLUB

粤菜 · 舒适
Cantonese · Cosy

这家高级粤菜厅由来自伦敦的皇朝集团开设，以供应鲍鱼、鱼肚等海味及海鲜等高级广东菜式为主。厨师注重选材用料，部分菜式用上独家从英国进口的食材，例如苏格兰龙虾。午膳时间可品尝各款自制广东点心。在传统节日，更有自制应节食品如粽子、月饼等出售。

Operated by London's Royal China Group, this Cantonese restaurant specialises in dried seafood like abalone and fish, along with other assorted seafood dishes. The quality of the seafood is good, with some of the ingredients imported from the UK, such as lobsters from Scotland. Dim sum is popular at lunch and, during Chinese festivals, handmade products like glutinous rice dumplings and mooncakes are provided.

山茶花

SAZANKA

铁板烧·典雅

Teppanyaki · Elegant

坐落于花园饭店的顶层，这日式铁板烧餐厅设有两个用餐区，皆可眺望城市美景，但大厨就在眼前灵巧地烹调食物，食客大概再无暇欣赏窗外景色。点选套餐是明智之举，可尝到大厨的不同手艺和各种食材，例如大部分套餐都有的小龙虾和雪龙黑牛。

On the top floor of the Okura Garden Hotel sits their discreet and comfortable teppanyaki restaurant. It is divided into two rooms and there are pleasant city views, but most of the attention of the customers is firmly on the chefs and their dextrous knife work. The best way of getting a good all-round experience is by opting for one of the set menus; most of which include both baby lobster and 'Xuelong Gyu' beef.

TEL. 6415 1111
黄浦区茂名南路58号花园饭店33楼
33F, Okura Garden Hotel,
58 South Maoming Road, Huangpu
www.gardenhotelshanghai.com

■ 价钱 **PRICE**
午膳 Lunch
套餐 set ¥ 388-488
点菜 à la carte ¥ 500-1,600
晚膳 Dinner
套餐 set ¥ 598-1,298
点菜 à la carte ¥ 500-1,600

■ 营业时间 **OPENING HOURS**
午膳 Lunch 11:30-14:00 (L.O.)
晚膳 Dinner 17:30-21:30 (L.O.)

黄浦区 **HUANGPU**

P ○II

TEL. 3376 8223

黄浦区蒙自路33号
33 Mengzi Road, Huangpu

■ 价钱 PRICE
晚膳 Dinner
点菜 à la carte ¥ 300-900

■ 营业时间 OPENING HOURS
晚膳 Dinner 17:30-21:30 (L.O.)

■ 休息日期 ANNUAL AND WEEKLY
CLOSING
农历新年休息7天
Closed 7 days Lunar New Year

¶○

SCARPETTA

意大利菜・舒适
Italian・Cosy

Scarpetta有靴子 —— 意国的形状 —— 和食物美味到令人舔嘴咂舌之意。这不光点明了餐馆的主题菜，大概也是厨师的祈愿吧？餐室占地两层，以鲜艳色彩和木作素材的装潢塑造出轻松随意的氛围。招牌菜包括铺满黑松露的和牛生牛肉薄片及风味特别的蛤蜊披萨，煎冰岛比目鱼也值得试试，自家制的披萨及意粉更是不容错过。

Colourful and fun, this Italian restaurant is spread over two floors and takes its name from the act of using a piece of bread to mop up the last bit of sauce on your plate. You certainly won't want to waste anything on your plate here, especially with their more unusual dishes like pizza vongole and Wagyu beef carpaccio with black truffle. Homemade pizza and pasta are not to be missed.

🍴

上海餐厅

SHANGHAI

沪菜・亲密

Shanghainese • Intimate

作为以专营蟹宴闻名全国的王宝和酒家的姊妹店,上海餐厅同样以高素质的本帮菜而家喻户晓。优质的食材加上用心烹调制作的一道道经典上海菜式,风味传统,令人回味再三。每逢大闸蟹当造季节,餐厅同样有蟹宴供应。食客可在店内购买店家自酿的黄酒或其他材料回家亲自下厨。

Perched on the second floor of the Central Hotel is this sister restaurant to the famed hairy crab restaurant, Wang Bao He. You'll find this speciality here in season but it's equally known for its authentic Shanghainese cooking. Their classic dishes use quality ingredients and are prepared with care. One highlight is the house-manufactured yellow rice wine, which you can buy to take home with you, along with various other ingredients.

 ♿ 🍽 ⇔12 🍴

TEL. 5396 5000

黄浦区九江路555号
王宝和大酒店2楼

2F, Central Hotel, 555 Jiujiang Road, Huangpu

■ 价钱 **PRICE**
午膳 Lunch
点菜 à la carte ¥ 150-650
晚膳 Dinner
点菜 à la carte ¥ 150-650

■ 营业时间 **OPENING HOURS**
午膳 Lunch 11:30-13:45 (L.O.)
晚膳 Dinner 17:30-21:45 (L.O.)

黄浦区 **HUANGPU**

TEL. 5308 5396

黄浦区广东路17号外滩3号2楼

2F, Bund 3, 17 Guangdong Road, Huangpu

www.unicoshanghai.com/ccc/

■ 价钱 PRICE
晚膳 Dinner
点菜 à la carte ￥500-600

■ 营业时间 OPENING HOURS
晚膳 Dinner 18:00-23:00 (L.O.)

■ 休息日期 ANNUAL AND WEEKLY CLOSING
週日休息
Closed Sunday

THE CHOP CHOP CLUB

烤肉餐馆・型格

Meat and Grills・Design

每天晚上，每十五分钟便有两款烤好的食物出炉，食客必须紧盯大荧幕，留意心仪菜肴的出炉时间，否则便可能与之擦身而过。这是Paul Pairet在魔都的第三家餐厅，概念是将食物在最佳时间，即刚出炉时呈献给食客，为此特地从英国订购Bertha烤炉，其炭烧效果出色，香气扑鼻。食物出场排序每天不同，Bertha's shitake不能错过。

You may think you can order food any time you want in a restaurant, but chef Paul Pairet disagrees. At the Chop Chop Club, meat mains are cooked on a schedule. Two mains and some sides appear on the giant screens every 15 minutes every night. Like a bidder in an auction, hungry guests compete for their favourite mains before they're sold out. 'Bertha's shitake' is highly recommended.

THE PINE AT RUI JIN

时尚欧陆菜 · 典雅

European contemporary · Elegant

餐厅位于古色古香的庭园中，环境舒适优雅。主厨虽年轻但经验丰富，宏愿是揉合中西饮食文化精粹，并为被忽略的寻常食材赋予新面貌，故着重选用源自本地的食材，以欧式烹调手法炮制成美馔，并会按季节和时令食材变更餐单。波士顿龙虾饭不得不试；前菜青瓜看似简单，厨师巧手处理下却是唤醒味蕾的清新之选。

The young chef aims to use modern techniques to shine a light on basic yet beautiful ingredients that go unnoticed, in a blend of East meets West flavours. The elegant dining room is surrounded by Chinese gardens that impart serenity. The tasting menus change regularly to reflect the seasons. The 'Cucumber' appetiser is bound to leave you feeling refreshed and the Boston lobster rice is not to be missed. Attentive service adds to the experience.

TEL. 6015 9268

黄浦区瑞金二路118号
瑞金洲际酒店11号楼

Building 11, InterContinental Ruijin Hotel, 118 Ruijin Er Road, Huangpu

■ 价钱 **PRICE**
午膳 Lunch
套餐 set ¥ 298-698
晚膳 Dinner
套餐 set ¥ 598-1,198

■ 营业时间 **OPENING HOURS**
午膳 Lunch 12:00-14:00 (L.O.)
晚膳 Dinner 18:30-21:00 (L.O.)

■ 休息日期 **ANNUAL AND WEEKLY CLOSING**
农历新年5天及周一休息
Closed 5 days Lunar New Year and Monday

黄浦区 **HUANGPU**

HUANGPU 黄浦区

P ⟷12 ⬦⬦

TEL. 5321 0321

黄浦区北京东路99号
益丰·外滩源3楼

**3F, Yi Feng Galleria,
99 East Beijing Road, Huangpu**

www.wtysh.com

■ 价钱 PRICE
午膳 Lunch
套餐 set ¥788-2,880
晚膳 Dinner
套餐 set ¥1,880-3,880

■ 营业时间 OPENING HOURS
午膳 Lunch 11:30-13:30 (L.O.)
晚膳 Dinner 17:30-21:00 (L.O.)

■ 休息日期 ANNUAL AND WEEKLY
CLOSING
农历新年休息3天
Closed 3 days Lunar New Year

🍴⦿

空蝉
UTSUSEMI

日本菜·传统
Japanese · Traditional

沿着满布石春的楼梯拾级而上,经过走廊上的和风
灯饰,再推开以日本唐纸所造的门,便到达洋溢京都
气息的房间。这儿奉行不时不食宗旨,每周三次将食
材从日本空运而来,厨师亦会亲自到市场选购,再按
食材拟定餐单。简单如木鱼花汤所用的水,也经多次
测试才敲定;食具由艺术家赵春设计和烧制,各个环
节皆尽显匠心。建议预约。

One of the best known Kaiseki restaurants in
Shanghai, UTSUSEMI boasts discreet service,
authentic Japanese décor and exquisitely
presented omakase meals in its four private
rooms. The chef has 20 years of experience
and insists on using only the best, yet not
necessarily the most expensive, items that
day for every course. Most ingredients are
flown in from Japan three times a week and
reservations are recommended.

蔚景阁

WEI JING GE

粤菜 · 经典

Cantonese · Classic

蔚景阁置身于充满历史感的上海总会旧址内，装潢免不了受到其怀旧风影响：复古的横梁雕木、沈稳的中式地毯、画功细致的壁画，令你仿如身处上世纪三、四十年代的高级中菜食府。来自香港的大厨凭经验和天赋制作出多道烹调精细、风味尤佳的粤菜和数道经典沪菜。周末早午点心拼餐经常一座难求。

Exposed ceiling rafters add to the sense that you're eating in a hidden attic at the Waldorf Astoria. This formal restaurant is enhanced by some big pieces of reproduction art, including a large mural. The Hong Kong born chef delivers a sophisticated Cantonese menu that showcases his talents, as well as number of classic Shanghainese specialities prepared with equal care. The weekend dim sum is always popular, so be sure to book early.

30

TEL. 6322 9988

黄浦区中山东一路2号
华尔道夫酒店5楼

5F, Waldorf Astoria Hotel,
2 Zhongshan Dong Yi Road, Huangpu

www.waldorfastoriashanghai.com

■ 价钱 **PRICE**

午膳 Lunch
套餐 set ¥ 300-400
点菜 à la carte ¥ 350-650
晚膳 Dinner
套餐 set ¥ 600-800
点菜 à la carte ¥ 350-650

■ 营业时间 **OPENING HOURS**

午膳 Lunch 11:30-14:30 (L.O.)
晚膳 Dinner 17:30-22:30 (L.O.)

■ 休息日期 **ANNUAL AND WEEKLY CLOSING**

七夕及平安夜休息
Closed Chinese Valentine's Day and Christmas Eve

TEL. 5383 9032

黄浦区雁荡路14号

14 Yandang Road, Huangpu

■ 价钱 **PRICE**

点菜 à la carte ¥ 10-20

■ 营业时间 **OPENING HOURS**

06:00-21:00 (L.O.)

味香斋（黄浦）

WEI XIANG ZHAI (HUANGPU)

面食·简朴

Noodles · Simple

雁荡路上的味香斋已伫立超过八十年，故不难看见门面满是老店的古旧痕迹，尽管如此，餐室自营业一刻便被食客挤得满满，吸引他们的是那多年不变、充满怀旧味道的面食。当中最受欢迎的要数麻酱面和辣肉面，排骨年糕也值得一试，在炎热的夏天，冷面则是消暑的明智之选。

For over 80 years customers have been flocking here to Yandang Road for the palate-pleasing taste of noodles. No one seems to mind eating in a congested, somewhat tired room – just as long as the flavour in the bowl remains unchanged. The sesame sauce noodles and spicy pork noodles are among the popular choices – but it's also worth trying the pork chop rice pudding. In summer they serve chilled noodles.

馨源楼

XIN YUAN LOU

粤菜 · 典雅

Cantonese · Elegant

餐厅坐落于瑞金洲际酒店主楼旁的一幢三层红砖西式洋楼中，划为茶室、客厅、酒吧和多个独立包厢，四周布满中式艺术品、火炉、古典风格的吊灯及家具，洋溢着浓浓的老上海风情，顶层的景观露台更可俯瞰花园美景。这儿提供粤菜和本帮菜，黑松露鸡、玻璃明虾炒蛋白、日式特酱鳕鱼等均是受欢迎菜式。

A 1920s French colonial-style villa plays host to this Cantonese restaurant boasting plenty of old world charm thanks to its period furniture, fireplace and Chinese artwork. It's spread over two floors and includes a bar, a lounge, a tea room and several private rooms. The menu is mostly Cantonese but there are some Shanghainese dishes, with popular choices being pan-fried chicken with black truffle, and sautéed crystal shrimps with egg white.

TEL. 6472 5222

黄浦区瑞金二路118号瑞金洲际酒店

**InterContinental Ruijin Hotel,
118 Ruijin Er Road, Huangpu**

www.intercontinental.com

■ 价钱 **PRICE**

午膳 Lunch
套餐 set ¥ 300-400
点菜 à la carte ¥ 210-740
晚膳 Dinner
套餐 set ¥ 400-500
点菜 à la carte ¥ 210-740

■ 营业时间 **OPENING HOURS**

午膳 Lunch 11:30-14:00 (L.O.)
晚膳 Dinner 17:30-22:00 (L.O.)

黄浦区 **HUANGPU**

P 24

TEL. 6311 2323

黄浦区黄陂南路338号新天地

Xintiandi, 338 South Huangpi Road, Huangpu

www.elite-concepts.com

■ 价钱 **PRICE**

午膳 Lunch
点菜 à la carte ¥ 150-400
晚膳 Dinner
点菜 à la carte ¥ 150-600

■ 营业时间 **OPENING HOURS**

午膳 Lunch 11:30-14:20 (L.O.)
晚膳 Dinner 17:30-22:20 (L.O.)

夜上海

YÈ SHANGHAI

沪菜 · 古典

Shanghainese · Historic

集团旗下夜上海品牌的第一家店子，开设在新旧交集的新天地一幢建于1928年的建筑内，供应的也是带有现代风味的上海菜，除了红烧肉、清炒虾仁、油爆虾等经典菜式，也有时令菜单，食材每天进货，确保其品质。餐厅有自家品牌的中国酒，爱好杯中物的你，可有兴趣尝尝？周末期间有现场演奏，增添用餐气氛。

There may be three other branches – in Hong Kong, Kowloon and Taipei – but this is the only one that occupies a historic property dating from 1928. Using special ingredients like Anji free-range chicken and spring bamboo, the Shanghainese cuisine is prepared in a modern style. The restaurant has its own label Chinese wine, and at weekends they lay on live music to accompany your dinner.

永兴
YONG XING

中国菜 · 简朴

Chinese · Simple

这店子隐藏于民居中一条细小的巷子里，不知就里的人容易错过。餐厅内墙壁贴上了红砖图案的墙纸，加上一道圆拱形的门，还有墙身的旧火炉，形成酷似地窖的环境，带着浓浓的怀旧味道。餐厅规模不大，但是食物水准不俗，且价钱相宜，江东鲈鱼炖姜丝值得一试。

This cozy little gem is hidden in a tiny alley and its non-descript façade makes it even harder to find. The archway and fireplace against red-brick wallpaper reminiscent of someone's home from a by-gone era set the tone for the warm welcoming service. Yong Xing serves delicious home-style Chinese food at wallet-friendly prices and is hugely popular among locals. Try steamed perch with shredded ginger in Jiangdong style.

TEL. 6473 3780

黄浦区复兴中路626弄1号
1 Lane, 626 Middle Fuxing Road, Huangpu

■ 价钱 **PRICE**
午膳 Lunch
点菜 à la carte ¥ 50-80
晚膳 Dinner
点菜 à la carte ¥ 50-80

■ 营业时间 **OPENING HOURS**
午膳 Lunch 11:00-13:30 (L.O.)
晚膳 Dinner 17:30-21:30 (L.O.)

黄浦区 **HUANGPU**

HOTELS
酒店

半岛

THE PENINSULA

奢华·个性

Grand Luxury · Personalised

这家声名显赫的酒店昂然傲立在外滩之上，上世纪三十年代的典雅风格完美地与现代美学筑构出细致华丽的格调，具品味的艺术装饰与时尚科技设施，塑造了典雅贵气的房间。完备的休闲设施令人乐而忘返，悠闲的下午从大堂茶座或宽敞明亮的泳池开始，晚上再到怀旧味浓的玲珑酒廊浅酌聊天，还有比这更惬意的事吗？

Occupying a commanding position on the Bund is this illustrious hotel, where 1930's elegance is blended with subtle modern stylings to create true luxury. Bedrooms showcase tasteful art deco design, with all technology carefully concealed. Afternoon tea in The Lobby, a swim in the stunning pool and a drink in the quirky Salon de Ning are experiences not to be missed.

TEL. 2327 2888

黄浦区中山东一路32号

32 Zhongshan Dong Yi Road, Huangpu

www.peninsula.com/shanghai

191 客房/**Rooms**
44 套房/**Suites**

双人房价格/**Price for 2 persons:**
￥ 3,000-4,000

餐厅推荐/**Recommended restaurants:**
逸龙阁 **Yi Long Court** ❀❀
艾利爵士 **Sir Elly's** ❀

黄浦区 HUANGPU

华尔道夫
WALDORF ASTORIA

古典·奢华

Historic · Grand Luxury

大堂的古典眺台、廊吧内前上海总会的豪华长吧台、曾为报章阅览室的浦江汇，令人神驰的旧上海氛围、在原貌上添了些时尚元素的装潢，令这家披着历史面纱的酒店份外引人入胜。华尔道夫临江套房不光坐拥醉人江河景色，更设有柱式大床，舒适度十足。酒店塔楼内的房间装潢现代瑰丽。

Perched on the Bund, this 20th century building conveys the charm of a bygone era, thanks to its distinctive hall, galleries, Long Bar and Salon de Ville. But walk through the Peacock Alley lounge and you'll find yourself surrounded by a far more contemporary style of design. These contrasting looks continue in the bedrooms. Service is attentive and meticulous.

TEL. 6322 9988

黄浦区中山东一路2号
2 Zhongshan Dong Yi Road, Huangpu

www.waldorfastoriashanghai.com

207 客房/**Rooms**
53 套房/**Suites**

双人房价格/**Price for 2 persons:**
¥ 2,400-2,550

餐厅推荐/**Recommended restaurants:**
Pelham's
蔚景阁 Wei Jing Ge

和平饭店
FAIRMONT PEACE

古典・艺术

Historic • Art Deco

于1929年开业的和平饭店是市内最具标志性的酒店，内里举目皆是的艺术珍品尽显奢华和个性。其套房声名显赫，客房亦同样典雅舒适。餐饮选择多元化，上海餐厅龙凰厅或西餐厅华懋阁（Cathay Room）均享负盛名，到爵士吧浅尝一杯或到茉莉酒廊享受下午茶是旅客的必然之选。酒店亦设水疗设施和泳池。

Opened in 1929, this iconic hotel's original Art Deco design is just one element that sets it apart. The Nine Nation themed suites are sure to impress, although all bedrooms are equally charming. Foodies will find much to savour – from Shanghainese food at Dragon Phoenix and afternoon tea in the Jasmine Lounge to the European menu in the Cathay Room. To really relax, try the Willow Stream Spa.

TEL. 6138 6888
黄浦区南京东路20号
20 East Nanjing Road, Huangpu
www.fairmont.com/peace-hotel-shanghai

232 客房/**Rooms**
38 套房/**Suites**
双人房价格/**Price for 2 persons:**
¥ 2,350-2,550

黄浦区 HUANGPU

95

TEL. 5368 8888

黄浦区中山东二路538号

538 Zhongshan Dong Er Road, Huangpu

www.wandahotels.com

177 客房/**Rooms**
13 套房/**Suites**

双人房价格/**Price for 2 persons:**
¥ 1,800-3,888

餐厅推荐/**Recommended restaurants:**
游宴一品淮扬 River Drunk

万达瑞华
WANDA REIGN

豪华·个性

Luxury · Personalised

色彩丰富的油画和置于大堂中央的鲜红色钢琴，装潢蛮有艺术味道。以樱桃木、大理石和高级家具布置的房间，典雅豪华，全部客房设有Bose音响器材，大部分房间还设有空气过滤器。房间内的迷你酒吧会按客人的喜好准备饮料，除含酒精的饮品外，一律免费。套房内更设有按摩椅。

Eye-catching design and attention to detail are the hallmarks of this stylish hotel, which opened in 2016. It offers great views, a variety of restaurants from Huaiyang to French, and every modern facility you'd expect. The bedrooms are very sleek and boast Bose sound systems; even the contents of the mini-bars are tailor-made to the wishes of the arriving guests.

浦发银行 | 信用卡
SPD BANK | Credit Card

有梦·敢享

浦发信用卡邀您开启美食之旅
—— 饕餮美食福利等你享！——

扫码立即办卡
开启你的美食之旅！

客服热线 400-820-8788
ccc.spdb.com.cn

安达仕
ANDAZ

商务·型格

Business · Design

酒店大堂放眼尽是现代感建筑,中央悬垂着一个由日本建筑师设计的金属建筑,别树一帜。餐厅选择丰富,从位于金属建筑内的日式餐厅、咖啡店,以至有现场音乐演奏的酒吧,式式俱备。客房的落地窗户让城市景观尽收眼底,你更可以iPad操控房间内所有电子设备,尽享科技之便。

The suspended steel structure in the lobby that houses a Japanese restaurant makes this design hotel unlike any other. Dining choices are numerous and include a modern coffee shop and a bar with live music. Along with iPad-controlled electronics, you can expect great city views from the bedrooms, thanks to the floor to ceiling windows. The facilities come complete with an I-spa.

TEL. 2310 1234

黄浦区嵩山路88号

88 Songshan Road, Huangpu

www.andazshanghai.com

260 客房/**Rooms**

47 套房/**Suites**

双人房价格/**Price for 2 persons:**

¥ 1,500 -3,000

黄浦区 **HUANGPU**

瑞金 洲际

INTERCONTINENTAL RUIJIN

连锁式·个性

Chain · Personalised

从历史走进现代，这家酒店原名为马立斯花园，由英国大亨于十九世纪兴建，后来曾为国家领导人官邸和接待外宾的瑞金宾馆，许多名人曾于此歇宿，是魔都有名的历史建筑。偌大的房间，布置融合现代科技与古典欧洲风格，气派独特，感觉舒适。面向花园的房间，更是清幽宁静。

TEL. 6472 5222
黄浦区瑞金二路118号
118 Ruijin Er Road, Huangpu
www.intercontinental.com

172 客房/**Rooms**
44 套房/**Suites**
双人房价格/**Price for 2 persons:**
¥ 1,800-2,200

餐厅推荐/**Recommended restaurants:**
馨源楼 Xin Yuan Lou ⅠO

The hotel is made up of different buildings – the newest having opened in 2013 and the oldest being a former State Guest House dating from 1917 – and is located in a park in the heart of the former French Concession neighbourhood. The rooms have a 19th century European-inspired look, albeit with all necessary mod cons – for a quiet one, ask to be on the garden side.

明天广场JW万豪
JW MARRIOTT TOMORROW SQUARE

商务·实用

Business · Functional

位于魔都的心脏地带，毗邻人民公园，交通便利，酒店特设会议套餐，是商务团体的绝佳之选。设在38楼的大堂，坐拥上海北部的醉人景色。已全面翻新的客房均备有60吋大电视和咖啡机，布置简约时尚，设备完善，窗外景色更是迷人。

Conveniently located next to People's Park, this hotel is ideal for business and leisure travellers. The lobby on the 38th floor catches gorgeous views of the city. All recently-renovated rooms come with a 60-inch flat-screen TV and a coffee machine. Other facilities include the world's highest library and indoor and outdoor pools. Conference packages are available for business meetings.

TEL. 5359 4969
黄浦区南京西路399号
399 West Nanjing Road, Huangpu
www.jwmarriottshanghai.com

267 客房/**Rooms**
75 套房/**Suites**
双人房价格/**Price for 2 persons:**
¥ 1,280-2,800

黄浦区 HUANGPU

酒店 HOTELS

黄浦区 HUANGPU

♿ 🅿 🛗 ⛊ 🖼 💇 🛗

TEL. 2312 9888
黄浦区西藏中路555号
555 Middle Xizang Road, Huangpu
shanghaimarriott.com

608 客房/**Rooms**
56 套房/**Suites**
双人房价格/**Price for 2 persons:**
¥ 1,200-2,000

雅居乐万豪
MARRIOTT CITY CENTRE

商务·時尚
Business · Contemporary

以水为题的大型壁画及华丽璀灿的水晶灯饰，使大堂看起来别具特色。作为一家商务酒店，除了会议设施和宴会场地外，还设有设备完善的健身中心，方便住客在繁忙会议过后能尽情舒展筋骨、放松绷紧了整天的肌肉。客房装潢清新时尚，设施尽善尽美。行政客房面积较宽敞。

The smart lobby and strikingly lit winter garden will certainly raise your expectations when you arrive at this large, well-equipped contemporary hotel. Diners are well looked after, with Cantonese cuisine served in Man Ho and Japanese in EZO. Along with extensive event and meeting facilities it also offers a comprehensive fitness centre and Touch Spa.

朗廷
THE LANGHAM

豪华·型格

Luxury · Design

朗廷酒店集团向以走在潮流尖端见称，这家位于上海著名旅游点的酒店当然也不例外。粉色伦敦出租车和24小时管家服务为你带来崭新的住宿体验。房间布置却一点不花巧，朴实的装潢，配上一幅能让你观看新天地独特风貌的玻璃窗，简单舒适。想好好享受闲暇时光，不妨享用水疗中心服务或到新吧浅尝一杯。

If you're going to stay here then it's certainly worth doing it properly, so take advantage of their pink London cab and their shopping butler! Follow that with afternoon tea in the Lobby Lounge or head off to the Chuan Spa for a bit of therapy. Bedrooms overlook the trendy Xintiandi district and the outside XTD bar is the perfect place to end the day.

TEL. 2330 2288

黄浦区马当路99号新天地

Xintiandi, 99 Madang Road, Huangpu

www.langhamhotels.com/shanghai

335 客房/Rooms
22 套房/Suites

双人房价格/Price for 2 persons:
¥ 1,650-2,400

餐厅推荐/Recommended restaurants:
唐阁 T'ang Court ✳✳

黄浦区 HUANGPU

101

黄浦区 HUANGPU

♿ 🛏 🚗 🅿 🛎 🕤 🍴

TEL. 6080 0800

黄浦区人民广场汉口路740号

740 Hankou Road, People's Square, Huangpu

www.theyangtzehotel.com

96 客房/**Rooms**
7 套房/**Suites**

双人房价格/**Price for 2 persons:**
¥ 1,100-3,600

🏠

扬子

THE YANGTZE

精品酒店·艺术

Boutique hotel · Art Deco

建于1934年，原为有远东第三大酒店之称的扬子饭店，也是当时的名人集中地。2007年经修葺后由朗廷集团管理，更名为扬子精品酒店，并于2013年易手予衡山集团运营。客房的装潢布置基本上保留了原来的面貌，大部分客房均设有阳台，能观赏生气勃勃的上海城市景色。大堂内的玫瑰廊充满旧上海情调。

When the hotel opened in 1934 it was "the third largest hotel in the Far East" and Rose Court was the meeting place for celebrities and the elite. Nowadays the hotel provides comfortable and spacious accommodation, thanks to its last refurbishment, which saw many of the rooms knocked together to create larger ones. The original balconies add to the period feel.

威斯汀
WESTIN BUND CENTER

商务·实用

Business · Functional

高耸的大堂内遍布棕榈树和水池，令人恍若置身热带园林之中。围绕着大堂可以找到自助餐厅和悦榕庄水疗中心。客房分布于两幢塔楼内，行政楼的房间宽敞豪华，而皇冠楼风格则较富现代感。你可于水晶苑享受中国美食，钟情意大利菜的话，帕戈意大利餐厅可让你一饱口福。

The huge atrium lobby, water feature and palm trees in the lounge area combine to create a tropical garden atmosphere. The buffet restaurant and the impressive Banyan Tree Spa add to the relaxing vibe. Bedrooms are split between two towers – Grand is luxurious; Crown has more of a contemporary style. For dining, you have a choice of classic Cantonese or Italian cuisine.

TEL. 6335 1888

黄浦区河南中路88号

88 Middle Henan Road, Huangpu

www.westinshanghai.com

287 客房/**Rooms**
271 套房/**Suites**

双人房价格/**Price for 2 persons:**
¥ 1,000-3,100

餐厅推荐/**Recommended restaurants:**
帕戈 Prego ⅠⅠ○

黄浦区 **HUANGPU**

103

♿ 🅿 🚗 ⚡ ⛷ 🖼 ⛷

TEL. 5353 8888

黄浦区九江路505号

505 Jiujiang Road, Huangpu

www.wbh-sh.com

321 客房/**Rooms**
32 套房/**Suites**

双人房价格/**Price for 2 persons:**
¥ 988-1,680

🏠

上海大酒店

GRAND CENTRAL

商务·实用

Business · Functional

酒店最为人津津乐道的，是其宽敞舒适的阳台式大堂，想像一下，坐在棕榈树下，聆听着从咖啡酒廊传来的清脆琴音，感觉多么写意自在！中法混合的装潢陈设让客房充满贵气，喜欢安静的住客，可选择较后方的房间。酒店的健身设施中设有斯诺克球桌，斯诺克爱好者可在此一展身手。

A hugely impressive balconied lobby is the main feature of this well-located hotel; relax under the palm trees and listen to the piano in the lounge and café. Bedrooms offer a good level of comfort and come in a mix of French and Chinese styles; ask for a quieter one at the rear of the hotel. Unusually for a fitness centre, it includes a snooker table.

英迪格
INDIGO

连锁式·时髦
Chain · Trendy

酒店位于外滩南端,占尽地利,黄浦江畔两岸景色尽收眼帘。明亮的布艺装饰、老上海街景油画、怀旧砖墙,客房的设计时尚中带有浓烈的殖民时代氛围。欲欣赏秀丽江河景色,可选择江景房或外滩全景套房。七楼的室内泳池以落地玻璃窗围绕,让你畅泳之余同时饱览醉人景致。

For the best views, ask for a river or Bund side bedroom at this stylish hotel. Bright coloured rugs and fabrics, exposed brick and reproduction paintings all add to the character and charm of the bedrooms. On the 6th floor you'll find a pleasant library lounge, along with the comfortable breakfast room. The individually designed suites are ideal for longer stays.

TEL. 3302 9999
黄浦区中山东二路585号
585 Zhongshan Dong Er Road, Huangpu
www.hotelindigo.com/shanghai

161 客房/**Rooms**
23 套房/**Suites**
双人房价格/**Price for 2 persons:**
¥ 1,580-1,880
餐厅推荐/**Recommended restaurants:**
恰 Char ⑩

花园饭店
OKURA GARDEN

连锁式·实用

Chain · Functional

酒店由两幢建筑物组成，分别是建于1926年带着巴洛克风格的法国俱乐部原址和在1980年兴建的大楼。整体风格偏向朴实、原始和功能性。房间内基本设施一应俱全，有园景和街景可供选择。特别的是，酒店内的食水和洗澡用水全经过净化，令住客感到放心。环境舒适的泳池是酒店的亮点。

There are two buildings that make up this Japanese chain hotel: a baroque-style former French sports club, built in 1926, which hosts the lobby, a coffee shop and ballroom; and a 33-storey building from the '80s which houses the soberly decorated bedrooms – ask for one on the garden side. The hotel purifies its own water, even for the showers.

TEL. 6415 1111

黄浦区茂名南路58号
58 South Maoming Road, Huangpu

www.gardenhotelshanghai.com

435 客房/**Rooms**
36 套房/**Suites**

双人房价格/**Price for 2 persons:**
¥ 1,188-2,000

餐厅推荐/**Recommended restaurants:**
山茶花 Sazanka ⅰⓞ

水舍·上海南外滩
THE WATERHOUSE AT SOUTH BUND

精品酒店·独特
Boutique hotel · Unique

简约、实用是这家精品酒店的设计主题：破裂的水泥墙身与昏暗的灯光，悬垂在天花上的仿古铁艺吊灯，大堂的装潢低调得来颇有格調。灰溜溜的砖墙、淺棕色的木地板……充满原始和粗犷味道的房间，吊诡地予人素净舒适的感觉，型格的玻璃浴室更替房间增添了几分趣味。坐拥明媚城市风光的天台阳台只在春天开放。

Bare concrete, steel girders and exposed brick mean that utilitarian chic is the order of the day at this design hotel set in a former army barracks. The bedrooms are understated and not without a certain style, with their stark white walls and glass cube bathrooms – ask for one overlooking the river. The lounge doubles as a bar and the roof terrace offers city views.

TEL. 6080 2988
黄浦区毛家园路1-3号
1-3 Maojiayuan Road, Huangpu
www.waterhouseshanghai.com

16 客房/**Rooms**
3 套房/**Suites**
双人房价格/**Price for 2 persons:**
¥ 1,100-1,500

餐厅推荐/**Recommended restaurants:**
欧社 Oxalis

黄浦区 HUANGPU

c8501089/iStock

静安区
JINGAN

RESTAURANTS
餐厅

❀❀ ❀

新荣记（南阳路）Ⓝ

XIN RONG JI (NANYANG ROAD)

台州菜·古典

Taizhou · Historic

餐厅位于历史悠久的贝轩大公馆，餐室四周以中国传统图案装饰，放眼满是古董摆设和建筑设计师贝聿铭的手绘作，别具特色。作为新荣记旗下的高档次食府，餐厅会为每一桌客人度身制作菜单，且食材每天以专车由台州送抵，客人须提早订座。其中用料珍贵的野生小黄鱼是招牌菜式。

Part of a hotel remodelled from a heritage building circa 1934 and the most prestigious outlet of the chain. The space is dotted with antiques and original drawings by the architect I.M.Pei. Most ingredients are shipped daily from Taizhou to ensure freshness. Its speciality braised wild-caught yellow croaker is steeply priced due to its scarcity. A menu is custom-made for every party in advance. Reservations are mandatory – no 'walk-ins'.

♿ 🍴 🅿 🚪14 ◐🍶

TEL. 6289 1717

静安区南阳路170号
170 Nanyang Road, Jingan
www.xinrongji.cc

静安区 JINGAN

■ 价钱 **PRICE**
午膳 Lunch
套餐 set ￥400-500
晚膳 Dinner
套餐 set ￥600-1,200

■ 营业时间 **OPENING HOURS**
午膳 Lunch 11:00-14:00 (L.O.)
晚膳 Dinner 17:00-21:00 (L.O.)

■ 休息日期 **ANNUAL AND WEEKLY CLOSING**
农历新年休息7天
Closed 7 days Lunar New Year

静安区 JINGAN

P ⇔16 ⓒ🍴

TEL. 3253 2299

静安区南京西路1601号
越洋广场5楼

**5F, Park Place,
1601 West Nanjing Road, Jingan**

■ 价钱 PRICE
点菜 à la carte ¥ 300-500

■ 营业时间 OPENING HOURS
11:00-22:00 (L.O.)

大董海参店（静安）
DA DONG (JINGAN)

中国菜 · 时尚
Chinese · Contemporary décor

这家在高级办公楼内的大董分店，一如其姊妹店以白色为主调、搭配时尚的装修，不同的是空间较大、包厢也较多。餐厅内常出现这个情境：穿着整齐制服的厨师，在客人桌旁切烤鸭，每一桌也如是。一碟碟皮脆肉嫩的鸭子，光看看已叫人垂涎。除了驰名烤鸭外，其他菜式也是精工烹调，如烩牛尾，十分出色。

Like its sister, this Da Dong has a bright and colourful appearance but it can also boast of being a lot bigger and having a larger number of private rooms. It's certainly not difficult to work out what the speciality of the house is – everywhere you look you'll see a uniformed chef slicing a roast Peking duck by someone's table. There are, however, plenty of other worthy dishes – not least the braised oxtail.

IL RISTORANTE - NIKO ROMITO

意大利菜·时髦

Italian · Fashionable

餐室采纳大量天然光，皮制沙发面向落地玻璃窗，让人饱览黄浦江景色。天花的水晶灯衬托着四周佩戴珠宝的模特儿照片，尽显奢华时尚。餐厅由经验丰富的意籍主厨主理，与其他宝格丽旗下餐厅一样，以精湛厨艺为食客带来正宗意大利风味。特别推荐自家制面包、意大利云吞和香煎鳌虾。

The floor-to-ceiling windows provide unobstructed views of the river and Pudong skyline. An array of crystal pendant lamps and semi-circular leather booths double as modern art. Just like its namesakes in Dubai and Beijing, this kitchen is supervised by the renowned chef Niko Romito. The food shows well-honed skills, precise execution and authentic Italian flavours. The house-made ravioli is divine and so is the grilled scampi.

TEL. 3606 7788

静安区河南北路33号
宝格丽酒店47楼
**47F, Bvlgari Hotel,
33 North Henan Road, Jingan**
www.bulgarihotels.com/shanghai

■ 价钱 **PRICE**
午膳 Lunch
套餐 set ￥398-1,100
点菜 à la carte ￥600-1,000
晚膳 Dinner
套餐 set ￥1,100-1,688
点菜 à la carte ￥600-1,000

■ 营业时间 **OPENING HOURS**
午膳 Lunch 12:00-14:30 (L.O.)
晚膳 Dinner 18:00-22:30 (L.O.)

静安区 JINGAN

静安区 JINGAN

 ♿ 🍴 🅿 🍷16 🚗 📶🍽️

TEL. 2216 6988

静安区常德路1号璞丽酒店2楼

2F, The PuLi, 1 Changde Road, Jingan

www.thepuli.com

■ 价钱 PRICE

午膳 Lunch
套餐 set ￥198-588
点菜 à la carte ￥350-1,500
晚膳 Dinner
点菜 à la carte ￥350-1,500

■ 营业时间 OPENING HOURS

午膳 Lunch 12:00-14:30 (L.O.)
晚膳 Dinner 18:00-22:00 (L.O.)

✤

斐霓丝

PHÉNIX

法国菜·独特

French • Unique

位于璞丽酒店内的餐厅酒吧，随意独特的风格予人舒适的感觉。位于静安公园内，巨幅落地玻璃窗让园内的丛林树影尽收眼底。时令菜单上印着数款冷切肉的名字，还有健康味美的色拉，当然少不了油焖烤鸭肉、朗姆糕和可供二至三人享用的慢烤美利奴羊肩。午膳套餐价格实惠，值得一试。

Floor to ceiling windows frame the views of Jing'an Park from this stylish restaurant in the luxurious PuLi hotel. The modern French menu includes charcuterie, several healthy and flavoursome salads and carefully prepared main courses like roast and confit duck. There are dishes to share, like the slow-cooked lamb shoulder, and what better way is there to finish than with a rum baba? The set lunch menu is great value.

家全七福（静安）
SEVENTH SON (JINGAN)

粤菜 · 典雅

Cantonese · Elegant

嘉里中心的家全七福于2014年开业，与浦东店同出一脉，熟客都知道这家来自香港的高级粤菜厅背后的故事。这里供应的全是传统功夫粤菜，海味菜式、汤品、烧味，甚至一碟小炒都是精工细作的佳肴。午市提供逾三十款自家制作的点心。内部装潢贵气中带点怀旧味道。

After the success of their branch in Pudong, the Hong Kong based group behind these Cantonese restaurants opened this comfortable and traditionally decorated sister in 2014. It also delivers a traditional Cantonese menu, with the technical skills of the chef evident in dishes that range from dried seafood and soups to roast meats and stir-fries. At lunch they offer over 30 varieties of dim sum.

&♿ P ⇔16 🕐🍴

TEL. 6266 3098

静安区南京西路1515号
静安嘉里中心1期2楼E2-03
**Unit E2-03, 2F, Tower 1,
Jing An Kerry Centre,
1515 West Nanjing Road, Jingan**

www.seventhson.hk

■ 价钱 **PRICE**
午膳 Lunch
点菜 à la carte ￥300-600
晚膳 Dinner
点菜 à la carte ￥600-1,000

■ 营业时间 **OPENING HOURS**
午膳 Lunch 11:30-14:15 (L.O.)
晚膳 Dinner 17:00-21:45 (L.O.)

静安区 JINGAN

TEL. 6073 8477

静安区西藏北路198号大悦城北座9楼910铺

Shop 910, 9F, Joy City II North Tower, 198 North Xizang Road, Jingan

■ 价钱 PRICE
午膳 Lunch
套餐 set ¥78-200
点菜 à la carte ¥100-200
晚膳 Dinner
套餐 set ¥150-398
点菜 à la carte ¥100-200

■ 营业时间 OPENING HOURS
10:00-21:30 (L.O.)

ALMA

西班牙菜 · 时尚

Spanish · Contemporary décor

餐厅位处大悦城北座顶层，全城唯一屋顶摩天轮就在窗外徐徐转动，幻变的灯光晕染四周，用餐环境独特！餐盘之上，厨师呈上的是价格亲民的创意西班牙料理，推介用料新鲜的西班牙炒饭，虾肉大而鲜甜、虾头满是虾膏，味道香浓，米饭的软硬度有正宗（较硬）和软身两种，由你决定。面包由餐厅新鲜烘焙，不要错过。

Spanish cuisine with a contemporary flourish is the feature here at this buzzy, well-priced and nicely run all-day restaurant. From the nine different homemade breads to specialities like 'Oh La La' – a dish using three kinds of tomato along with foie gras, quail's egg and Iberico ham – it's clear this is a confident kitchen. The only rooftop Ferris wheel in town that sits right beside the restaurant adds to the charm.

鼎泰丰（上海商城）
DIN TAI FUNG (SHANGHAI CENTRE)

沪菜・舒适

Shanghainese・Cosy

在全球拥有逾百家店子的鼎泰丰，光在上海便已有十家分店，这家店子开设在上海商城的波特曼丽嘉酒店内，装潢较其他姊妹店讲究。招牌小笼包当然是必吃之选，糕点餐单内的芋泥小笼包和豆沙小笼包等颇特别。此外，全年均有以大闸蟹作馅料的小笼包供应。

With a portfolio of over 100 restaurants and counting, it is clear that this international chain is doing something right. There are 10 branches in Shanghai and this one is probably the most comfortable, although it is somewhat hidden in the Shanghai Centre. Along with the speciality – their wonderful Xiao Long Bao – are some hairy crab dishes. You can even have dumplings for dessert, with red bean paste or chestnut.

P ⇔10 ◎🍴

TEL. 6289 9182

静安区南京西路1376号
上海商城1楼104A铺

**Shop 104A, Shanghai Centre,
1376 West Nanjing Road, Jingan**

■ 价钱 **PRICE**
点菜 à la carte ¥ 130-460

■ 营业时间 **OPENING HOURS**
11:00-21:00 (L.O.)

静安区 **JINGAN**

🏠 **P** ⟷12 ☺🍴

TEL. 6287 5001

静安区愚园路68号晶品6楼605

**Shop 605, 6F, Crystal Galleria,
68 Yuyuan Road, Jingan**

■ 价钱 **PRICE**

午膳 Lunch
套餐 set ￥48
点菜 à la carte ￥100-200
晚膳 Dinner
点菜 à la carte ￥100-200

■ 营业时间 **OPENING HOURS**

午膳 Lunch 10:30-14:00 (L.O.)
晚膳 Dinner 17:00-21:30 (L.O.)
周末 Weekend
10:30-21:30 (L.O.)

😋

文兴酒家
FOUR SEASONS

粤菜·舒适

Cantonese · Cosy

位于晶品购物中心内的文兴酒家，设有小酒吧和户外用餐区，主用餐区以仿古红砖配以木纹地板和木制家具，充满怀旧气息。小厨房内挂满整幅玻璃窗的烧味在提醒你：这是广东菜馆！完备的菜单内全是大家熟悉的粤菜如烧味、蒸煮小菜或小炒、煲仔菜和海鲜等，一应俱全，烧鸭和炒龙虾是其招牌菜。

Its red brick walls, tufted booth seats and solid wood furniture may not fit in the stereotype of a Cantonese restaurant. But its menu is unmistakably Cantonese – meat, veggies and seafood all meticulously roasted, steamed, stir-fried or braised. Try their signature dishes such as the famous crispy duck, and stir-fried lobster with ginger and scallion.

静安区 **JINGAN**

功德林（静安）
GONG DE LIN (JINGAN)

素食·东方
Vegetarian · Oriental décor

要数上海知名的老字号菜馆，当然少不了功德林，多年来追随者众。菜单上写着的是鳝、鸭、鸡等，碟子上放着的看似鱼、有的像肉，却是货真价实的素菜。厨师的妙手将豆腐和菇菌等素食材料造出不同形状、外型吸引的菜式，以假乱真的功夫真令人拍案叫绝！招牌菜如黄油蟹粉绝对不能错过！

No inventory of restaurants in Shanghai can be complete without Gong De Lin. It opened in 1922 and, even though it is perhaps the most famous of the city's vegetarian restaurants, you can still hear customers doubting whether it is truly vegetarian when they see words like 'eel' and 'chicken' on the menu and see the mock-meat on their plate. It makes clever use of soy products and mushrooms and is also suitable for vegans.

⇔15 Ⓞⵎ
TEL. 6327 0218
静安区南京西路445号
445 West Nanjing Road, Jingan
www.shgodly.com

■ 价钱 **PRICE**
午膳 Lunch
点菜 à la carte ¥ 80-150
晚膳 Dinner
点菜 à la carte ¥ 80-150

■ 营业时间 **OPENING HOURS**
午膳 Lunch 11:00-14:00 (L.O.)
晚膳 Dinner 17:00-21:00 (L.O.)

静安区 JINGAN

静安区 JINGAN

🅿 ⇔12 ⃝

TEL. 6247 7677

静安区巨鹿路768号巨富大厦1楼

1F, Jufu Mansion, 768 Julu Road, Jingan

■ 价钱 PRICE

午膳 Lunch
点菜 à la carte ¥ 200-300
晚膳 Dinner
点菜 à la carte ¥ 200-300

■ 营业时间 OPENING HOURS

午膳 Lunch 11:00-14:00 (L.O.)
晚膳 Dinner 17:00-21:30 (L.O.)

🙂

南麓·浙里（静安）
LE PATIO & LA FAMILLE (JINGAN)

杭州菜·时尚

Hangzhou · Contemporary décor

餐室简单而现代，与其姐妹店一样供应的是精致的杭州菜。与四川中路店相比，这儿有不少独家招牌菜式，例如奉化芋艿羹、腐皮黄鱼卷，还有用上四个半小时焖制的文火焖小牛肉。这店另一特色是餐单提供一人分量的餸菜，例如招牌菜迷你富贵火方，想大快朵颐何用呼朋唤友？

Le Patio & La Famille on Julu Road has a sister restaurant on Middle Sichuan Road. The modern sleek interior here may appeal to regulars in similar ways, but its menu offers slightly different Hangzhou food from its sister branch. Courses that used to be available only in big portions are now made in individual servings. Exclusive offerings at this location include minced pork soup with egg white and coriander and simmered beef with sweet soy sauce.

Shinho 欣和

待世界如家人

Treat the world as family

企业的价值观植根于欣和经营事业的初衷和使命
我们所有的事业都围绕"家"这个核心理念展开
待世界如家人
这个理念驱动着我们的价值观
我们也不遗余力地用这些价值观去感染每一位合作伙伴

The concept of family is core to how we do business. Family is at the
heart of everything we do and this notion drivers our values and how
we partner with everyone we work with.

尚牛社会
BEEF & LIBERTY

美国菜 · 亲密

American · Intimate

这儿的牛肉汉堡采用塔斯曼尼亚的草饲牛，每天早上和下午以手工制作，保证新鲜。店内选用的食材大部分从英国进口，面包是自制的，前菜的脆皮炸鸡条用的是无激素的鸡腿肉。建议尝尝培根芝士汉堡和黑椒香浓汉堡。店子有特别的啤酒供应。

There are times when only a burger will do – and, for those times, there is Beef & Liberty. The kitchen uses Tasmanian grass-fed beef which is ground in-house twice a day, in time for lunch and dinner, and served in their homemade buns. They also do good sides, salads and sliders and use hormone-free chicken along with condiments imported from the UK such as ketchup...and the beer is pretty good too.

TEL. 6289 5733

静安区南京西路1376号
上海商城111铺

Shop 111, Shanghai Centre,
1376 West Nanjing Road, Jingan

www.beef-liberty.com

■ 价钱 **PRICE**
午膳 Lunch
套餐 set ¥ 89-139
点菜 à la carte ¥ 70-150
晚膳 Dinner
点菜 à la carte ¥ 70-150

■ 营业时间 **OPENING HOURS**
11:00-22:30 (L.O.)

静安区 JINGAN

P ⇔14 ⊙🌢

TEL. 5228 1133

静安区南京西路1038号
梅龙镇广场7楼719

**Unit 719, 7F, Westgate Mall,
1038 West Nanjing Road, Jingan**

www.crystaljade.com

■ 价钱 **PRICE**
午膳 Lunch
点菜 à la carte ¥ 100-120
晚膳 Dinner
点菜 à la carte ¥ 180-200

■ 营业时间 **OPENING HOURS**
午膳 Lunch 11:00-14:30 (L.O.)
晚膳 Dinner 17:00-21:30 (L.O.)

■ 休息日期 **ANNUAL AND WEEKLY
CLOSING**
农历新年休息3天
Closed 3 days Lunar New Year

🍴⊙

翡翠酒家（静安）

CRYSTAL JADE (JINGAN)

粤菜·舒适

Cantonese · Cosy

在熙来攘往的南京西路上逛得倦了，正好到这家粤菜餐厅大快朵颐。餐厅时尚明亮，在此用膳格外舒适。菜式揉合传统和创新，包括烧味、煲仔菜、海鲜和小炒，同时亦有自制点心供应。由于隶属新加坡集团，故也能尝到新加坡特色菜如辣椒蟹等。

A shopping mall at West Nanjing Road is home to this bright Cantonese restaurant which benefited from a redecoration in 2015. The chef delivers a classic Cantonese menu that includes roast meats, casseroles, seafood and stir-fried dishes, but he isn't afraid of adding his own innovative touches. As it's under the ownership of a Singapore group, the restaurant also offers some Singaporean specialities like chilli crab.

福一零八八

FU 1088

沪菜·古典

Shanghainese · Historic

餐馆位于一幢建于上世纪二十年代的洋房内,装潢陈设保留了原来风貌:怀旧的瓷砖地台、精致的雕花木墙、新添置的古董摆设和典雅的水晶灯,是浓浓的老上海氛围。菜牌上供应的也是充满老上海味道的菜式,香溢红烧肉、老上海熏鱼是招牌菜。晚饭时间设有个人最低消费规定。

A beautiful tiled entrance, wood panelling and striking light fittings are some of the original features of this 1920s townhouse. You'll dine in one of 16 private rooms dotted around the house, all of which are decorated in a traditional way. The menu provides a comprehensive range of classic Shanghainese dishes. Try the braised pork with soy and rock salt, or the deep-fried fish. Be aware that there is a minimum spend.

🍴 🛋18 🍽

TEL. 5239 7878

静安区镇宁路375号
375 Zhenning Road, Jingan

■ 价钱 **PRICE**
午膳 Lunch
点菜 à la carte ¥ 400-600
晚膳 Dinner
点菜 à la carte ¥ 500-800

■ 营业时间 **OPENING HOURS**
午膳 Lunch 11:00-14:00 (L.O.)
晚膳 Dinner 17:30-23:00 (L.O.)

静安区 **JINGAN**

静安区 JINGAN

🏠 **P**

TEL. 5228 9961

静安区康定路1025号
1025 Kangding Road, Jingan

■ 价钱 PRICE
午膳 Lunch
套餐 set ¥ 25-35
点菜 à la carte ¥ 100-400
晚膳 Dinner
点菜 à la carte ¥ 100-400

■ 营业时间 OPENING HOURS
午膳 Lunch 11:00-13:50 (L.O.)
晚膳 Dinner 17:00-22:30 (L.O.)

■ 休息日期 ANNUAL AND WEEKLY CLOSING
农历新年休息6天
Closed 6 days Lunar New Year

🍴🍽

滇道

LEGEND TASTE

云南菜 · 异国风情

Yunnan · Exotic décor

小小的店子，连大厨在内，全店的员工均来自云南，供应的是简单却道地的云南菜，且以各式各样的杂菌和香料闻名于魔都。拥有逾十年经验的大厨在为此店掌厨前，一直在云南当地的食肆工作。招牌菜小米辣炒牛肉和竹筒山珍带给你实实在在的云南风味。

For those craving something a little more adventurous, this Yunnan restaurant may well hit the spot. It's undeniably simple in both décor and style of service but the chef, who worked in his native Yunnan before coming here in 2008, prepares a cuisine in which mushrooms and herbs are used extensively. The two dishes to try both boast splendidly enticing names: sautéed spicy minced beef with mint taste, and Yunnan multifarious mushroom soup.

汉舍中国菜馆（静安）
MADAM ZHU'S KITCHEN (JINGAN)

中国菜 · 亲切
Chinese · Neighbourhood

店如其名，汉舍中国菜馆的室内布置能带给你家的感觉：宽敞的空间、背靠着红砖墙的小书柜、小而舒适的沙发、雅致的瓷砖地台和色彩斑斓的玻璃窗，一片暖洋洋的氛围。菜单包含川菜和沪菜，如果木烤鸭、熏鲳鱼、葱油鸡等，味道甚佳。

Although it's located in a shopping mall, the exposed brick, tiles, bookcases and stained glass window add genuine warmth and colour to this large room. Sichuan and Shanghainese dishes are the mainstay of the menu and dishes are simply prepared, full of flavour and affordably priced. Look out for Madam Zhu's specialty roast duck; steamed chicken in scallion oil sauce; and fried smoked pomfret in soy sauce.

P ⇄40 ☏⑪

TEL. 6231 8819

静安区万航渡路889号
悦达889广场3楼20号

**L3-20, Yueda 889 Square,
889 Wanhangdu Road, Jingan**

■ 价钱 **PRICE**
午膳 Lunch
点菜 à la carte ¥ 150-200
晚膳 Dinner
点菜 à la carte ¥ 200-300

■ 营业时间 **OPENING HOURS**
午膳 Lunch 11:00-14:00 (L.O.)
晚膳 Dinner 17:00-21:00 (L.O.)

静安区 JINGAN

  P ⟷12 ◔ 🍴 ⌘

TEL. 2203 8889

静安区延安中路1218号
静安香格里拉大酒店4楼

**4F, Jing An Shangri-La Hotel,
1218 Middle Yan'an Road, Jingan**

www.shangri-la.com/jingan

■ 价钱 **PRICE**
午膳 Lunch
套餐 set ¥ 158-598
点菜 à la carte ¥ 490-1,800
晚膳 Dinner
点菜 à la carte ¥ 490-1,800

■ 营业时间 **OPENING HOURS**
午膳 Lunch 11:30-14:30 (L.O.)
晚膳 Dinner 18:00-22:30 (L.O.)

🍴

1515牛排馆
1515 WEST CHOPHOUSE

扒房·亲密

Steakhouse · Intimate

舒适的长沙发搭配深色木装饰的酒吧,格调高雅,
适合餐前浅酌,周末更有现场乐队演奏。主餐室内,
最引人注目、也是餐厅焦点的是开放式的烧烤厨房。
来自澳洲的牛排被风干后以炭火烤煮,口感与味道
俱佳。经典菜如凯撒色拉、牛肉塔塔、美国乳酪蛋糕
等,均能在此品尝得到。

They've certainly nailed the classic American
look at this nicely styled chophouse. Start with
a cocktail in the masculine, wood panelled bar
before passing by the inviting bakery into the
restaurant. All the favourite steakhouse dishes
are here, from Caesar salad mixed at the table
to steak tartare and cheesecake. However, it's
the grill that takes centre stage – the various cuts
of dry-aged Australian beef are chargrilled to
perfection.

四季轩
SI JI XUAN

沪菜・豪华
Shanghainese • Luxury

餐厅坐落于同名酒店的中心地带，店内传统的装潢、惹人注目的水族箱和艺术品营造出轻松的用餐氛围。餐桌以真翡翠餐具布置，配上新鲜兰花，环境舒适宜人。餐单由祖籍上海的主厨主理，除了各式传统上海菜，亦可找到广东菜肴。

Located on the second floor of the Four Seasons hotel, this restaurant features a classic interior along with an impressive aquarium – watching the fish swim by adds to the relaxing feel. Every table is adorned with lovely fresh orchids and jade tableware. The native Shanghainese chef offers a classic menu that reflects his origins, although there are also some Cantonese dishes on offer.

TEL. 6256 8888
静安区威海路500号四季酒店2楼
2F, Four Seasons Hotel,
500 Weihai Road, Jingan
www.fourseasons.com/shanghai

■ 价钱 PRICE
午膳 Lunch
点菜 à la carte ¥ 400-1,000
晚膳 Dinner
点菜 à la carte ¥ 400-1,000

■ 营业时间 OPENING HOURS
午膳 Lunch 11:30-14:15 (L.O.)
晚膳 Dinner 17:30-21:45 (L.O.)

静安区 JINGAN

静安区 JINGAN

 ♿ 🅿 ⇔24 ◐ 🍴 ⚜

TEL. 2203 8888

静安区延安中路1218号
静安香格里拉大酒店3楼

**3F, Jing An Shangri-La Hotel,
1218 Middle Yan'an Road, Jingan**

www.shangri-la.com/jingan

■ 价钱 PRICE
午膳 Lunch
套餐 set ¥ 125-138
点菜 à la carte ¥ 120-300
晚膳 Dinner
套餐 set ¥ 388-800
点菜 à la carte ¥ 300-700

■ 营业时间 OPENING HOURS
午膳 Lunch 11:30-14:15 (L.O.)
晚膳 Dinner 17:30-21:30 (L.O.)

🍴◯

夏宫

SUMMER PALACE

粤菜・豪华

Cantonese・Luxury

餐馆分为三个区域：供应点心的厨房区、提供传统经典砂锅菜的灯笼厅及专侍精细高级经典粤菜的皇家厅。有品质的高级家具摆设及雅致的装潢，室内环境高贵且有气派。高素质的食物水准，在大后方担任指挥工作、富经验的香港主厨应记一功。优秀的酒单用来接待珍贵的客人最适合不过。

There are three distinct areas to this smart and sumptuously decorated Cantonese restaurant, with each one serving its own speciality. In the Pantry you'll find dim sum; it's claypot classics in the Lantern; and the Imperial for sophisticated and classic Cantonese cooking which is overseen by a chef with many years' experience in Hong Kong. The private dining rooms are very impressive, as is the wine list.

食社

THE COMMUNE SOCIAL

西班牙菜 · 型格

Spanish · Design

餐厅地址原是巡捕房，兴建于1910年代，外墙是清水红砖，室内布置却简约时尚，感觉舒适。以流行烹饪手法烹调的菜式，保留了传统西班牙菜的特色。海胆配夏巴塔面包抹山羊芝士黄油是店中比较受欢迎的菜式；晚膳设每日精选菜单，厨师会不定期更新。店内唯有二楼的包厢接受订座，但需收取服务费。

A former police station circa 1910 is now home to a tapas bar exuding minimalist chic, complete with a terrace. The chef reinvents the classics with modern techniques and exotic flavours. Try their ciabatta with Korean sea urchin, goat's cheese and capsicum; or the Iberico pork and foie gras burger. Daily specials are also offered at dinner. Reservations are accepted for the private room only, for which there are additional service charges.

🏠 ⬭20 🚗 🚫📶

TEL. 6047 7638

静安区江宁路511号

511 Jiang-Ning Road, Jingan

www.communesocial.com

■ 价钱 **PRICE**
午膳 Lunch
套餐 set ￥188-250
点菜 à la carte ￥200-300
晚膳 Dinner
点菜 à la carte ￥250-300

■ 营业时间 **OPENING HOURS**
午膳 Lunch 12:00-14:30 (L.O.)
周末午膳 Weekend lunch
11:30-14:30 (L.O.)
晚膳 Dinner 18:00-22:30 (L.O.)

■ 休息日期 **ANNUAL AND WEEKLY CLOSING**
农历新年3天、中国传统节日、周日晚膳及周一休息
Closed 3 days Lunar New Year & Chinese festivals, Sunday dinner and Monday

静安区 **JINGAN**

静安区 JINGAN

P ↔12 ⊙📷

TEL. 6261 4333

静安区延安西路396号3楼
3F, 396 West Yan'an Road, Jingan

■ 价钱 PRICE
点菜 à la carte ¥ 200-500

■ 营业时间 OPENING HOURS
11:00-22:00 (L.O.)

🍴🍽

惠食佳（静安）
WISCA (JINGAN)

粤菜·舒适

Cantonese · Cosy

广州的惠食佳把精致创新的粤菜带到上海，共有两家
分店。静安区这家店子环境雅致，大厅以鱼池和竹子
营造出安逸平静的氛围，桌子与桌子之间保持着充足
空间，包厢设在上层。这里最受欢迎的是海鲜菜式，
鱼、虾、蟹等均有多种不同的方法烹调。驰名的一系
列煲仔菜也不能错过。

The Wisca group originated in Guangzhou and
now has two branches in Shanghai serving their
Cantonese specialities. This one comes with a
fish pool and plenty of bamboo which lend a
certain serenity to proceedings. The seafood
dishes are the most popular choices on the
menu although the famed casseroles are also
well worth ordering. There are private rooms
available upstairs.

渝信川菜（静安）

YUXIN SICHUAN DISH (JINGAN)

川菜 · 简朴

Sichuan · Simple

集团在魔都的总店，自1993年运营以来，便以风味正宗的优质川菜享誉全国。餐馆设在一幢办公大楼内，经由扶手电梯到达。甫踏进门内，热情而有效率的服务生会将你领到座位前。菜单上有大量经典四川菜式供应，当中的川北凉粉和两江麻辣鱿鱼令你没齿难忘。

Since opening in 1993 this large restaurant – the original branch – has built a well-deserved reputation for the quality of its Sichuan dishes. It's located in an office block; escalators lead you up to its entrance where the efficient staff are on hand to guide you to a table or booth. The extensive menu offers plenty of classic dishes; try the clear noodles in chilli sauce and the Two Rivers Mandarin fish.

🚭 ⇧20

TEL. 5298 0438

静安区成都北路333号
招商局广场3楼

3F, ZhaoShangJu Square, 333 North Chengdu Road, Jingan

www.yuxin1997.com

■ 价钱 **PRICE**
午膳 Lunch
点菜 à la carte ¥ 50-200
晚膳 Dinner
点菜 à la carte ¥ 50-200

■ 营业时间 **OPENING HOURS**
午膳 Lunch 11:00-14:00 (L.O.)
晚膳 Dinner 17:00-21:30 (L.O.)

静安区 JINGAN

静安区 **JINGAN**

HOTELS
酒店

静安香格里拉
JING AN SHANGRI-LA

奢华 · 奢华

Grand Luxury · Grand Luxury

酒店位处静安区的核心，身处其中还能眺望毛主席生前的官邸！大堂内的波浪形天花、素雅的大理石地台、如瀑布般从上奔流至地上的水晶珠帘，典雅与奢华并蓄。以现代风格作主调的客房，隐约带点中式元素，雅致舒适。繁忙过后，能在水疗中心享受一下贴心的服务，夫复何求！

In the heart of Jingan is one of the city's newest hotels, which overlooks a former residence of Chairman Mao. The striking lobby, with its marble floor and curtain of crystals, sets the tone of sophisticated luxury that pervades the hotel. There's a subtle Chinese element to the contemporary look of the bedrooms; those on floors 30 or above enjoy great city views.

TEL. 2203 8889
静安区延安中路1218号
1218 Middle Yan'an Road, Jingan
www.shangri-la.com/jingan

466 客房/**Rooms**
42 套房/**Suites**

双人房价格/**Price for 2 persons:**
¥ 1,488-2,688

餐厅推荐/**Recommended restaurants:**
1515牛排馆 **1515 West Chophouse** ⑪
夏宫 **Summer Palace** ⑪

静安区 JINGAN

静安区 JINGAN

♿ 🍸 🏊 🚗 💇 🏋 📶 🧖 SPA 💪

TEL. 3606 7788

静安区河南北路33号

33 North Henan Road, Jingan

www.bulgarihotels.com/shanghai

63 客房/**Rooms**
19 套房/**Suites**

双人房价格/**Price for 2 persons:**
¥ 3,400-4,600

餐厅推荐/**Recommended restaurants:**
Il Ristorante - Niko Romito ✿

宝格丽 Ⓝ
BVLGARI

豪华·浪漫
Luxury · Romantic

酒店毗邻历史建筑，距附近名胜只是十分钟路程，并能饱览外滩美景。大堂装潢细致高雅，各处展示了名贵珠宝及五六十年代巨星的经典照片，更添高贵格调。宽敞的房间内放置了意大利设计的家具，更备有手工玻璃杯，用以享受你酒吧内的精选美酒实是尚佳享受。欲肆意放松，别忘了到华贵的按摩浴池，或来一客全日供应的早餐犒赏自己。

This modern luxury hotel commands views of The Bund while tucked away from the busy traffic. From the vintage fashion photos to the fine jewellery of its namesake brand, the décor exudes an effortless charm that is unmistakably Roman. Spacious rooms are stylishly furnished with Italian design fittings. Wherever you go, service is thoughtful and warm. Breakfast is served all day.

璞丽
THE PULI

豪华·型格

Luxury · Design

高耸的天花、时尚的摆设、优秀的中国艺术装饰和落地玻璃窗外的苍翠竹树丛,甫走进酒店大堂已令你不想离开。融合了中国风与现代设计的房间,朴实而舒适,宽敞的开放式浴室令人神往。面向静安公园的房间景色较宜人。别忘了享用偌大的无边际泳池和采用中、印、泰三国古老秘方的水疗服务。

The lobby, with its Chinese art, high ceiling and modern furniture, really sets the tone of this strikingly original design hotel. On the same level you'll also find a cosy library and a delightful garden terrace. Local artwork and modern facilities combine to make the bedrooms bright, elegant and uncluttered. There's also a superb infinity pool and a charming spa.

TEL. 3203 9999
静安区常德路1号
1 Changde Road, Jingan
www.thepuli.com

193 客房/**Rooms**
36 套房/**Suites**
双人房价格/**Price for 2 persons:**
¥ 4,280-5,380

餐厅推荐/**Recommended restaurants:**
斐霓丝 Phénix ✿

静安区 JINGAN

静安区 JINGAN

  四季

FOUR SEASONS

商务·奢华

Business · Grand Luxury

坐落于静安区的心脏地带，这摩天大楼曾于2015年进行翻新，客房高雅舒适，可饱览繁华璀璨的上海市全景。酒店提供多元化的餐饮选择，大堂酒廊是市内受欢迎的下午茶之选，亦能找到上海和日本菜餐厅。水疗中心、室内泳池和健身设施一应俱全。

Located in the heart of Jing'an, the smart lobby lounge of this modern skyscraper is full of people who've flocked here for afternoon tea. Refurbished in 2015, the bedrooms are stylish and offer downtown city views. The health centre is well-equipped and has an indoor pool, making it ideal for business people looking to unwind after a long day's work.

TEL. 6256 8888

静安区威海路500号
500 Weihai Road, Jingan

www.fourseasons.com/shanghai

345 客房/**Rooms**
78 套房/**Suites**

双人房价格/**Price for 2 persons:**
¥ 1,400-2,500

餐厅推荐/**Recommended restaurants:**
四季轩 **Si Ji Xuan**

波特曼丽思卡尔顿
THE PORTMAN RITZ-CARLTON

商务·奢华

Business · Grand Luxury

坐落于上海心脏地带的波特曼丽思卡尔顿，耸立在上海展览中心之前，与名胜静安寺只有十分钟步行距离，不论是观光、购物或是公干，都十分方便。客房的布置虽简单却实用而舒适，部分房间更有不错的城市景观。劳碌过后，可到充满旧上海气息的酒吧放松心情，或在七楼的泳池和健身房锻炼筋骨。

For business types, this hotel sits in front of the Shanghai Exhibition Centre; for tourists it's just a ten minute walk to Jing'an Temple. The hotel, built in the '90s and renovated in 2015, offers soberly decorated but extremely comfortable bedrooms. The Ritz Bar has a charming, chic atmosphere; for the more energetic, there are two pools and a fitness centre.

TEL. 6279 8888

静安区南京西路1376号上海商城
Shanghai Centre,
1376 West Nanjing Road, Jingan
www.ritzcarlton.com/shanghai

547 客房/Rooms
46 套房/Suites

双人房价格/Price for 2 persons:
¥ 1,480-1,780

静安区 JINGAN

静安区 JINGAN

♿ 🚗 💈 🏊 📷 🆘 🧖

TEL. 6157 1688

静安区凤阳路601号

601 Fengyang Road, Jingan

www.kempinski.com/shanghai

244 套房/**Suites**

套房价格/**Price for Suites:**
¥ 1,000-2,000

🏠

御锦轩凯宾斯基
THE ONE BY KEMPINSKI

商务·时尚

Business · Contemporary

若你享受在旅程中入厨，御锦轩将是不二之选。这儿
只设套房，全部配备简易或完整厨房及厨具，非常适
合长期逗留，旅客可按需要选择一至三间房间。房间
装修以大理石为主，舒适时尚。若不喜入厨，琳琅满
目的送餐到房服务或酒店餐厅亦不会令你失望。健身
中心设备完善。

For cooking enthusiasts, these serviced
apartments, in a building with subtle art deco
elements, would be the choice. Choose from
suites with one, two or three bedrooms. All
are furnished in marble and equipped with
kitchenettes which make them perfect for long
stays. If you are reluctant to cook, there is an
extensive room service menu, bistro, bar and
lounge available.

艾本
URBN

精品酒店 · 环保

Boutique hotel · Eco-friendly

前身是旧仓库的艾本酒店以再生材料和本地资源装饰布置，是全国首家碳中和酒店。别致的庭院和正门前的绿色植物，充满了天然闲适的味道。接待处后由旧行李箱堆叠而成的牆别有韻味。以深棕色木板地台、原创家具摆设的房间，充满个性，且有园景和中庭景供挑选。只有二十六间客房，须及早预订。

China's first carbon neutral hotel is housed in a converted warehouse and uses only recycled and locally sourced materials – its unique features include a wall behind the front desk made out of old suitcases. Upstairs you'll find a large restaurant, while bedrooms are slick and original and look out either onto the atrium or the courtyard garden.

TEL. 5153 4600

静安区胶州路183号

183 Jiaozhou Road, Jingan

www.urbnhotels.com

24 客房/**Rooms**
2 套房/**Suites**

双人房价格/**Price for 2 persons:**
¥ 1,500-2,000

静安区 JINGAN

Юлия Моисеенко/iStock

长宁区
CHANGNING

RESTAURANTS
餐厅

菁禧荟

AMAZING CHINESE CUISINE

潮州菜·时尚

Chao Zhou · Contemporary décor

菁禧荟的地址实为一幢别墅,店内没有主餐室,只有五个房间,因此,预订座位是必须的,同时,为了确保能吃上喜欢的菜式,也必须要预订菜式。高级潮州菜如潮州滷水老鹅头,以养了三年的狮头鹅制作,还有鲜甜多膏的潮式冻花蟹,全都不能错过。潮式生腌红膏富贵虾只在时令季节才供应。

You'll need to plan ahead a little if you want to enjoy the Chao Zhou cuisine here at Amazing Chinese Cuisine. Making a booking is the first challenge as it only has five private rooms. Secondly, customers are encouraged to pre-order otherwise they'll find many of the menu's dishes are not available. Consider going for the marinated goose head; chilled crab Chao Zhou style; or seasonal offerings like marinated mantis shrimps.

⬡ ⬡16 ⬡⬡

TEL. 6262 5677

长宁区虹桥路1665号B5别墅

B5 Villa, 1665 Hongqiao Road, Changning

■ 价钱 **PRICE**
午膳 Lunch
点菜 à la carte ￥300-600
晚膳 Dinner
点菜 à la carte ￥800-1,200

■ 营业时间 **OPENING HOURS**
午膳 Lunch 11:00-14:00 (L.O.)
晚膳 Dinner 17:00-22:00 (L.O.)

长宁区 CHANGNING

143

🎐 ⇔24 ⬤🍴

TEL. 3980 9188

长宁区愚园路1037号
1037 Yuyuan Road, Changning

■ 价钱 **PRICE**
午膳 Lunch
套餐 set ¥580-880
晚膳 Dinner
套餐 set ¥580-880

■ 营业时间 **OPENING HOURS**
午膳 Lunch 11:10-13:15 (L.O.)
晚膳 Dinner 17:30-20:45 (L.O.)

✽

福和慧
FU HE HUI

素食・简约
Vegetarian・Minimalist

福集团在愚园路开了多家餐厅，福和慧的与别不同在于它是一家素菜馆，不论装潢或菜式都充满禅意。餐厅只供应套餐，每道菜都经过精心设计，兼顾偏爱口味浓淡的食客。新菜单中包含不少传统功夫菜；更有以不同中国茶搭配菜式的套餐，食客轻啖素菜之余可同时品味中国茶的姿彩。三层楼内全是独立厢房，环境宁静安逸。

This restaurant encompasses a serene Zen-inspired atmosphere that truly reflects the idea that veganism isn't just about the food, but is a way of life. Only set menus are served, with masterfully created and artfully presented dishes, including some old-fashioned labour-intensive recipes. Tea culture is also closely related to Zen, which is why the restaurant offers tea pairings where four different Chinese teas are served to complement the dishes.

S.PELLEGRINO
圣培露.

随星所遇

邂逅意式风格

全球品牌大使 黄轩

敬请关注官方微博与微信
新浪微博：@SPellegrino圣培露中国
官方微信：sanpellegrinochina

鹿园

MOOSE

淮扬菜 · 型格

Huai Yang · Design

餐厅坐落于一幢百岁洋房中,楼高三层,一楼为主餐室,二楼设有包厢,三楼则用来接待贵宾和举行筵席,更设有后花园。以白色为主调的餐室以欧式风格装潢,并配以店东妻子从欧洲拍卖行收购的古董家具和油画。在洋溢欧洲情调的餐厅中,餐单上却是正宗淮扬菜,主厨掌厨逾三十年,不要错过葱香脆皮猪婆参。

This century-old mansion, complete with a manicured backyard, was overhauled in 2018. While the antique furniture and retro oil paintings complement its long history, the all-white interior and antler wall pieces exude contemporary European charm. The head chef has over 30 years of experience in Huaiyang cuisine and his signature crispy white teat fish with scallion is not to be missed.

☺18 ◉¶

TEL. 6205 5058

长宁区新华路119弄1号

Lane 1, 119 Xinhua Road, Changning

■ 价钱 **PRICE**
午膳 Lunch
点菜 à la carte ¥ 300-500
晚膳 Dinner
点菜 à la carte ¥ 300-500

■ 营业时间 **OPENING HOURS**
午膳 Lunch 11:00-16:00 (L.O.)
晚膳 Dinner 17:00-21:00 (L.O.)

长宁区 **CHANGNING**

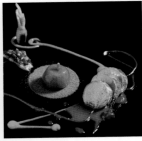

長寧区 CHANGNING

🅿 ⇄12 ⇎ ◐🍴 ⚬

TEL. N/A

长宁区镇宁路465弄161号1号楼
101-102室愚园里

**101-102, Building No. 1,
Garden Office, 465 Zhenning Road,
Lane No 161, Changning**

www.taian-table.com

■ 价钱 **PRICE**
晚膳 Dinner
套餐 set ￥ 1,088-1,388

■ 营业时间 **OPENING HOURS**
晚膳 Dinner 17:30-20:00 (L.O.)

■ 休息日期 **ANNUAL AND WEEKLY
CLOSING**
周日及周一休息
Closed Sunday and Monday

泰安门
TAIAN TABLE

创新菜・典雅
Innovative・Elegant

曾因选址闹得沸沸扬扬的泰安门，随着落户到宁静的
镇宁路重新出发。店子外表低调，只设小指示牌，拐弯
而进却是另一片天地：餐室面积宽广、楼底挺拔，中
间是设计简约的柜枱式餐桌。簇新的设施令目光不期
然投放到开放式厨房内、由德籍厨师史蒂芬・斯蒂勒
（Stefan Stiller）率领的团队身影之上。餐单每季更新，
只接受网上预约。

The restaurant in our 2017 guide was forced to
close for a couple of months. But now it's back
with a vengeance at a new location. Its signature
counter seating enclosing an island where the
chefs prepare food is still the key appeal, while
those looking for some privacy may pick the two
booths. Chef Stefan Stiller's signature creations
come only in 14-course set menus that change
every season. Online reservation is mandatory.

寻味巴黎 N

BISTRO BY YANNICK ALLÉNO

法国菜 · 法式小餐馆
French · Bistro

曾是圣玛利亚女子中学校舍，修缮后成为装潢时尚的餐厅。厨房是开放式设计，厨师们殷勤工作时的画面煞是有趣，经典法国乐韵悠悠响起令人意会这是一家法国餐厅。菜单选择丰富而传统，且按时令自家制作，猪鼻冻及鸡腿佐胡萝卜配多芬苹果值得一试，最后一定要点法式奶油吐司，外脆内软的吐司带焦香，简单而味道悠长。

The historic site of St. Mary's Hall is now home to a number of restaurants, including this modern bistro supervised by celebrated French chef Yannick Alléno. The menu captures the essence of Parisian cuisine while reflecting what's in season, such as rillettes, pig snout jelly terrine, chicken with grilled carrot and pommes dauphine. A dinner here is never complete without the quintessential bistro classic - brioche with vanilla ice-cream.

🛋 ⌂7

TEL. 6088 1677

长宁区长宁路1195号
长宁来福士广场4号古建6号商铺
Unit 6, H4 Building, Raffles City Changning, 1195 Changning Road, Changning

www.yannick-alleno.com

■ 价钱 **PRICE**
晚膳 Dinner
套餐 set ￥638
点菜 à la carte ￥350-800

■ 营业时间 **OPENING HOURS**
晚膳 Dinner 14:00-21:00 (L.O.)

长宁区 **CHANGNING**

TEL. 5237 9778

长宁区愚园路1015号
1015 Yuyuan Road, Changning

■ 价钱 PRICE
午膳 Lunch
套餐 set ¥ 800-1,280
晚膳 Dinner
套餐 set ¥ 1,000-1,500

■ 营业时间 OPENING HOURS
午膳 Lunch 11:00-13:30 (L.O.)
晚膳 Dinner 17:30-21:30 (L.O.)

福一零一五

FU 1015

沪菜 · 传统

Shanghainese · Traditional décor

老洋房搭配本帮菜像是上海餐饮业其中一个经典模式，福一零一五便是一家开在老洋房中的提供精致本帮菜的菜馆，其菜式中不乏老上海元素，包括以野生河虾制成的三虾豆腐，及选用散养草鸭的松仁酥鸭。屋内是一间间包厢，装潢怀旧优雅，置身其中让人有时光倒流的感觉！餐厅每晚有钢琴表演，必须预早订座。

The old villa is divided into small dining rooms and, while the décor is reminiscent of old Shanghai, the food re-creates classics in a decidedly modern way. 'Tofu with shrimp trio' is tofu stewed in shrimp soup and topped with shrimp roe, tomalley and shelled shrimps. Pine nut duck is marinated and deboned before being stuffed with shrimp paste and ground pine nuts and deep-fried. A pianist adds to the experience. Reservations are a must.

福一零三九
FU 1039

沪菜 · 简朴

Shanghainese · Simple

集团旗下首家食店，位于1921年兴建的古宅内，福一零三九的装潢充满旧中国风：古董摆设、怀旧灯饰、旧照片……阳台上的座位面向草园，份外舒适写意。与餐室的布置相仿，餐厅供应的是正宗而传统的上海菜。三楼全是私人厢房。贴心的服务、美味的菜肴和相宜的价钱，不错的用餐选择。

Unlike its two sisters, the original Fu focuses more on the local market by keeping to an authentic, traditional Shanghainese menu and having customer-friendly prices. What also sets it apart is the building in which it is located: it dates from the 1920s and its first owner was a French banker; it subsequently became a kindergarten before opening as a restaurant in 2006. It has a pleasant terrace, along with several private rooms.

🏠 🍽 ⇔16 🕐🍴
TEL. 5237 1878
长宁区愚园路1039号
1039 Yuyuan Road, Changning

■ 价钱 PRICE
午膳 Lunch
点菜 à la carte ¥ 200-600
晚膳 Dinner
点菜 à la carte ¥ 300-600

■ 营业时间 OPENING HOURS
午膳 Lunch 11:00-14:00 (L.O.)
晚膳 Dinner 17:30-23:00 (L.O.)

长宁区 CHANGNING

🗸 🅿 ⇔10 🍴

TEL. 5299 6279

长宁区遵义路150号
虹桥南丰城北区L506

L506, North Phase, SH The Place,
150 Zunyi Road, Changning

■ 价钱 PRICE
点菜 à la carte ¥ 80-100

■ 营业时间 OPENING HOURS
11:00-21:00 (L.O.)

■ 休息日期 ANNUAL AND WEEKLY
CLOSING
农历新年除夕休息1天
Closed 1 day Lunar New Year Eve

🍴

那时新疆·乌孙

NASHI XINJIANG · WUSUN

新疆菜·异国风情

Xinjiang · Exotic décor

铜壶和斑斓复古水晶吊灯令此新疆菜馆复古中不失时尚，且洋溢西域风情，用餐区更设有一辆西域古国马车，坐在里面吃饭让人仿如穿越古代，唯需预订。传统新疆风味的菜式分量豪迈，推介新疆大盘鸡，肥厚的鸡肉渗满了汤汁，异常鲜美；分量十足的超级馕坑肉焖得香嫩；散发独特果木香的红柳烤肉也是一绝，食客更可透过玻璃窗口直击烧烤过程。

This four-store chain boasts retro décor and exotic touches such as copper vessels and colourful glass lampshades. The menu is authentically Xinjiang and portion sizes are generous. Signatures include braised chicken with potato and green pepper, roasted meat with rose willow and big pit meat. Each branch has its own exclusive items on the menu; at this one 'Fish Market' is worth a try.

月半鸭

PHAT DUCK

粤菜·舒适

Cantonese · Cosy

月半鸭有"胖鸭"之意,以胖为名概因东主身形比较肥胖,而鸭则当然是指其招牌菜烤鸭。其烤鸭只选用45天大、重四斤二两的北京填鸭,厨师以特别调校的菜汁腌制两小时,以辟走鸭的腥味。烤鸭酱与传统的有所不同,特别加入了咖喱,吃起来更加惹味;鸭片佐以泰国虾片和花生芝麻黄糖也是一大特色。餐厅环境简洁舒适。

A restaurant specialising in Peking duck. The chef marinates 45-day-old ducks weighing exactly 2.1kg with puréed celery, ginger, spring onion, garlic and radish before they are roasted to perfection. The barbecue sauce served with the duck is also a secret blend and comes with a hint of curry. As well as cucumber and scallions, prawn crackers and ground peanuts with sugar and sesame are offered as condiments.

TEL. 5241 6602

长宁区长宁路890号玫瑰坊2楼F57
**F57, 2F, Metro Town,
890 Changning Road, Changning**

■ 价钱 **PRICE**
午膳 Lunch
套餐 set ￥58
点菜 à la carte ￥100-150
晚膳 Dinner
点菜 à la carte ￥100-150

■ 营业时间 **OPENING HOURS**
午膳 Lunch 11:30-14:30 (L.O.)
晚膳 Dinner 17:30-21:00 (L.O.)

■ 休息日期 **ANNUAL AND WEEKLY CLOSING**
农历新年6天及中国传统节日休息
Closed 6 days Lunar New Year and Chinese traditional festivals

长宁区 **CHANGNING**

🏠 ⬚40 📶 ⛱

TEL. 6241 9100

长宁区新华路321号

321 Xinhua Road, Changning

www.lebec.com.cn

■ 价钱 **PRICE**

午膳 Lunch
点菜 à la carte ￥400-900
晚膳 Dinner
点菜 à la carte ￥400-900

■ 营业时间 **OPENING HOURS**

午膳 Lunch 12:00-14:00 (L.O.)
晚膳 Dinner 18:00-22:00 (L.O.)

■ 休息日期 **ANNUAL AND WEEKLY CLOSING**

周二午膳及周一休息
Closed Tuesday lunch and Monday

🍴

VILLA LE BEC - BISTRO 321

法国菜・时尚

French • Contemporary décor

在古老洋房内的餐室，给分成四间各有特色的区域：简约小餐馆；有特色横梁天花的舒适小餐室；布置庄严、备有火炉的古典房间，还有面向园林的玻璃房。来自里昂的主厨所预备的全是经典法国小餐馆菜式，如五香猪鸡肉馅饼、干邑半熟鸭肝、烤牛带骨眼肉等。酒窖内的藏酒品质尤佳，蛮吸引。

A lovely renovated villa, dating from 1924, is home to this French bistro. It's divided into several rooms, all decorated differently: a simple bistro occupies the former garage; one cosy dining room has a charming beamed ceiling, another has a fireplace, and the garden terrace is a delightful spot on warm days. The classic bistro dishes include an excellent pâté en croute and côte de boeuf prepared barbecue style.

子福慧

ZIFU HUI

中国菜·舒适

Chinese · Cosy

供应精品江鲜粤菜的子福慧定位为高档私宴订制餐厅,标榜选用最新鲜的原材料、精细的烹饪技巧和不添加味精,以还原食材原味。其中江鲜皆来自有鱼米之乡美誉的南通。餐厅装潢风格与菜式相搭配,以"静"、"思"概念设计,简约中充满禅意,并设七间厢房。由于烧味及炖汤处理需时,建议先行预订。

This is haute couture in culinary terms – exquisite courses tailored to diners' liking. It specialises in river fish from Nantong, alongside up-market Cantonese fare. The freshest ingredients are skilfully prepared and MSG is banished from the kitchen. Besides the serene Zen-inspired main dining room, seven private rooms are available. As roast meats and double-boiled soups take time to make, reservations are highly recommended.

🛆 🍽 ♿14 🎵

TEL. 3388 7577

长宁区虹桥路1665号云峰别墅C2幢

**Building C2, Yunfeng Villa,
1665 Hongqiao Road, Changning**

■ 价钱 **PRICE**
点菜 à la carte ￥300-800

■ 营业时间 **OPENING HOURS**
11:00-22:00 (L.O.)

长宁区 **CHANGNING**

gionnixxx/iStock

徐汇
及闵行区

XUHUI &
MINHANG

RESTAURANTS
餐厅

✿✿ ✿✿

雍福会

YONGFOO ÉLITE

沪菜 · 经典

Shanghainese · Classic

餐厅建筑建于1930年，曾是前苏联、德国、越南和英国等国家的领事馆，后于2001年被购入并耗时三年改建为餐厅。小花园内的走廊由清朝的长廊顶所建，值得游览。菜单以古法本帮菜改良而成，例如加入茶叶以减油腻，以黑毛猪增加层次感。祁门红茶烟熏鳕鱼、普洱茶红烧肉均是特色菜。

The main building dates from 1930 and was the British Consulate before undergoing a major 3-year refurbishment and becoming a private club, which is filled with the owner's antique collection. The restaurant offers a Shanghainese menu to satisfy both traditionalists and those who prefer a more modern, lighter style of cuisine. Two dishes particularly worthy of attention are smoked codfish with Qi Men black tea, and braised pork in brown sauce.

🍴 💺20 🅿🍴 ♿

TEL. 5466 2727

徐汇区永福路200号

200 Yongfu Road, Xuhui

■ 价钱 **PRICE**
午膳 Lunch
套餐 set ¥ 680-2,000
点菜 à la carte ¥ 400-800
晚膳 Dinner
套餐 set ¥ 680-2,000
点菜 à la carte ¥ 600-1,000

■ 营业时间 **OPENING HOURS**
午膳 Lunch 11:00-13:45 (L.O.)
晚膳 Dinner 17:00-21:30 (L.O.)

■ 休息日期 **ANNUAL AND WEEKLY CLOSING**
农历新年6天及中国传统节日休息
Closed 6 days Lunar New Year and Chinese traditional festivals

徐汇及闵行区 XUHUI & MINHANG

P ⇔12 ◐📶

TEL. 5466 5758

徐汇区淮海中路999号
环贸广场6楼602号

**602, 6F, iapm,
999 Middle Huaihai Road, Xuhui**

■ 价钱 **PRICE**
点菜 à la carte ¥ 250-500

■ 营业时间 **OPENING HOURS**
11:00-22:00 (L.O.)

大董（徐汇）
DA DONG (XUHUI)

中国菜 · 时尚

Chinese · Contemporary décor

大董在上海开了几家分店，这家开设在地铁站上的商场内，许多时晚市在六时前已满座，如此宾客盈门全因为其驰名名烤鸭 —— 来自北京的鸭子给烤至皮脆肉嫩，以多款精细佐料伴吃，配上面饼和烧饼，确是与别不同。此外，另一道名菜葱烧海参也不能错过。多约几位朋友一起用膳，便能多尝几道菜。

Come in a large group so you can benefit from unconstrained ordering – that way you can experience the variety of dishes on offer at this busy Chinese restaurant. Having said that, few get past their signature roast duck – using duck from Beijing, it not only has wonderfully crisp skin and succulent meat but is served with a variety of accompaniments such as steamed or grilled buns. The braised sea cucumber with scallions is worth trying too.

吉品轩
JI PIN COURT

粤菜・典雅

Cantonese・Elegant

餐厅位于一幢法式古建筑内，尤如繁嚣闹市中的绿洲。主厨有超过二十年烹调经验，其对传统粤菜的掌握无庸置疑，难得是他仍致力推陈出新研发菜式。其招牌菜包括以特选矿泉水炖煮五至六小时的炖汤及用龙眼蜜制作的叉烧；还有流心富贵虾等海鲜菜式。餐厅设多款一人分量菜式及套餐。如欲一尝海鲜，建议订座时先作查询。

Remodelled from a heritage building in the former French Concession, this is a serene oasis amid the busy city centre. Chef Cheung has over 20 years of experience in Cantonese cooking and he is keen to imbue the cuisine with new elements. Attention to detail is clear in his cooking – soups are made with spring water and char siu is glazed in longan honey. Dim sum is served at lunch. Regulars tend to pre-order seafood when reserving.

TEL. 6469 9969
徐汇区乌鲁木齐南路55号3楼
3F, 55 South Wulumuqi Road, Xuhui

■ 价钱 PRICE
午膳 Lunch
套餐 set ¥ 248
点菜 à la carte ¥ 200-500
晚膳 Dinner
套餐 set ¥ 988-1,288
点菜 à la carte ¥ 500-800

■ 营业时间 OPENING HOURS
午膳 Lunch 11:00-14:30 (L.O.)
晚膳 Dinner 17:00-21:30 (L.O.)

徐汇及闵行区 **XUHUI & MINHANG**

TEL. 5466 9988

徐汇区建国西路480号
建业里嘉佩乐酒店

**Capella, Jian Ye Li,
480 West Jianguo Road, Xuhui**

www.capellahotels.com/shanghai/

■ 价钱 **PRICE**
午膳 Lunch
套餐 set ￥ 288-338
周末早午拼餐
Weekend brunch ￥ 488
晚膳 Dinner
套餐 set ￥ 1,088
点菜 à la carte ￥ 300-1,000

■ 营业时间 **OPENING HOURS**
午膳 Lunch 12:00-13:45 (L.O.)
晚膳 Dinner 18:00-21:45 (L.O.)
周五及周六晚膳
Friday and Saturday dinner
18:00-22:15 (L.O.)

🕸

LE COMPTOIR DE PIERRE GAGNAIRE

法国菜・型格

French・Design

上海最大的石库门清水红砖建筑群，是这装潢时尚法式餐馆的栖息处。用餐前后不妨到入口旁的酒吧浅酌一杯。主餐室灯光和煦，气氛谧静，主厨服务Pierre Gagnaire麾下多年，用心的选材，加上娴熟烹调技巧，奉上传统正宗、一丝不苟的法国菜肴，鸭肝冻、奶油牛蛙炖锅均不能错过。最后以甜品作结更添圆满。

A lively, laid-back brasserie from an iconic chef, located in an 'urban resort' hotel made up of restored red-brick houses dating from the 1930s. Be sure to have drinks in the sleek oval-shaped cocktail bar beforehand. The authentic French food doesn't disappoint: signature dishes like foie gras terrine, frog poulette cocotte are not to be missed. Save some room for dessert too.

利苑（徐汇）
LEI GARDEN (XUHUI)

粤菜·时尚

Cantonese · Contemporary décor

源自香港的利苑集团，业务遍布亚洲各地，提供高素质的正宗粤菜。员工每天都会亲自试菜，监控食材及食品的品质，确保点心、烧味、炖汤维持水准。不妨考虑以每天熬煮超过六小时的海鲜汤即席泡煮的过桥象拔蚌，或是即点即做的腊味煲仔饭。这家位处大型商场的分店装潢时尚，经常满座，建议在订座时同时预留烧味和炖汤等招牌菜。

The chain may be spreading rapidly in Asia but quality control is strictly imposed to ensure all dim sum, roast meats and double-boiled soups remain the same high standard as at the parent restaurant. This branch in a popular mall boasts a hip décor and is always full. 'Crossing-the-bridge' geoduck is blanched at your table in a hot seafood stock that took six hours to make. Claypot rice with preserved meat is made à la minute.

P ⇄15 ◎⊓

TEL. 5425 2283

徐汇区淮海中路999号
环贸广场4楼401号铺

**Shop 401, 4F, iapm,
999 Middle Huaihai Road, Xuhui**

■ 价钱 **PRICE**
午膳 Lunch
点菜 à la carte ￥150-500
晚膳 Dinner
点菜 à la carte ￥250-500

■ 营业时间 **OPENING HOURS**
午膳 Lunch 11:30-14:00 (L.O.)
晚膳 Dinner 17:30-21:00 (L.O.)

徐汇及闵行区 XUHUI & MINHANG

  P

TEL. 5470 0508

闵行区都市路5001号
仲盛世界商城4楼422号

**Shop 422, 4F, The Sky Mall,
5001 Dushi Road, Minhang**

■ 价钱 **PRICE**
午膳 Lunch
点菜 à la carte ￥90-110
晚膳 Dinner
点菜 à la carte ￥90-110

■ 营业时间 **OPENING HOURS**
午膳 Lunch 11:00-14:00 (L.O.)
晚膳 Dinner 17:00-21:00 (L.O.)

鹅夫人（闵行）
MADAM GOOSE (MINHANG)

烧味・新潮

Cantonese Roast Meats・Chic

餐厅装潢别具特色，从布置至食物均以鹅为主题，不能错过的烧鹅选用九十天大、产自广东的黑棕鹅，体重受严密监控，以保持品质，皮脆骨细、肉质嫩滑；由于供应量有限，晚市要尽早前往免扑空。此外，烧味及点心亦别出心裁，当中以菠萝油和天鹅叉烧酥为必试之选。等待出炉烧鹅的同时，不妨来一客椒盐鸭下巴。

Diners aren't really here for the purple velvet seats and white winged chandeliers – it's the food that keeps them coming back. For its signature roast goose, only 90-day-old birds from Guangdong at a certain weight are used to ensure quality. Other specialities include soy-marinated chicken, swan-shaped char siu pastry, buttered pineapple buns, and fried duck jaws in peppered salt. Roast geese are available in limited quantity so come early.

豪生酒家

HAO SHENG

沪菜 · 亲密

Shanghainese · Intimate

这简朴的店子提供的是传统上海菜，例如东坡肉、莴笋丝、白灼猪肝等，特别之处是没有菜单，到达时女东主会询问客人的喜好，再按食量和预算决定菜单，除非特别要求，否则全由厨师发办。女东主亲切友善，在此用膳有如回家吃饭般温暖。餐厅非常细小，只得数张桌子和一间厢房，建议预订。

The décor is nothing to write home about, but the authentic home-style Shanghainese fare – Dongpo pork, shredded celtuce, blanched pork liver – keeps the regulars coming. An à la carte menu is not available but the chef chooses for you according to your budget, allergies, preference and what's fresh. With only a few tables and one room, Hao Sheng fills up very fast and reservations are recommended.

¥ 10

TEL. 136 2174 1821

徐汇区广元路156号

156 Guangyuan Road, Xuhui

■ 价钱 **PRICE**

午膳 Lunch
点菜 à la carte ¥ 50-100
晚膳 Dinner
点菜 à la carte ¥ 50-100

■ 营业时间 **OPENING HOURS**

午膳 Lunch 11:00-14:00 (L.O.)
晚膳 Dinner 17:30-21:00 (L.O.)

TEL. 6282 9260

徐汇区天平路41号
41 Tianping Road, Xuhui

■ 价钱 **PRICE**
午膳 Lunch
点菜 à la carte ￥150-200
晚膳 Dinner
点菜 à la carte ￥150-200

■ 营业时间 **OPENING HOURS**
午膳 Lunch 11:30-14:00 (L.O.)
晚膳 Dinner 17:00-23:30 (L.O.)

吉士
JESSE

沪菜・简朴
Shanghainese・Simple

位于天平路上的老房子内，又名老吉士，小小的两层楼内每天都挤满食客，若不预早订座或会感到扫兴。能在古旧的房子内享用道地的老派本帮菜，别有一番风味，那怕环境狭窄拥挤了点也不相干。推荐菜式包括红烧肉、咸鸡和糖醋小排等充满旧上海味道的美食。

Lovers of authentic Shanghainese cuisine flock to this old house on Tianping Road – its décor and period feel providing the ideal backdrop. The dining room may be spread over two floors but it still gets a bit congested so it's worth arriving having made a booking. Dishes to go for include braised pork belly; salty chicken; and sweet vinegar ribs.

米泰
MI THAI

泰国菜·时尚

Thai · Contemporary décor

由泰籍厨师主理的传统泰国菜馆，每道菜都风味道地、正宗，且价格相宜。招牌菜包括冬阴功汤、绿咖喱鸡、猪颈肉和芒果糯米饭，味道鲜美。餐室的环境却以摩登、有个性和舒适取胜。主餐室因着开放式厨房而变得生气蓬勃，旁边连酒吧的餐室的氛围却是宁谧悠闲，与街上的闹哄哄形成强烈对比。

In a neighbourhood well stocked with cool cafés and stylish boutiques comes this popular, pared-down Thai restaurant. It's split between two rooms: one has an open kitchen; the other, an attractive timbered ceiling. The Thai chef keeps things fairly traditional so expect all the classics, from tom yum soup to green curry; but look out too for the grilled pork neck or mango served with sticky rice. The set lunch menu is great value.

☎🍴

TEL. 5403 9209

徐汇区安福路195号2楼
2F, 195 An Fu Road, Xuhui

■ 价钱 **PRICE**
午膳 Lunch
套餐 set ¥ 88-98
点菜 à la carte ¥ 150-300
晚膳 Dinner
点菜 à la carte ¥ 150-300

■ 营业时间 **OPENING HOURS**
午膳 Lunch 11:30-14:30 (L.O.)
晚膳 Dinner 17:30-22:30 (L.O.)

■ 休息日期 **ANNUAL AND WEEKLY CLOSING**
农历新年休息7天
Closed 7 days Lunar New Year

徐汇及闵行区 **XUHUI & MINHANG**

🚭 🅿 ⏰🍴

TEL. 6296 1091

闵行区都市路5001号
莘庄仲盛世界商城4楼418B

**418B, 4F, The Sky Mall,
5001 Doushi Road, Minhang**

■ 价钱 **PRICE**
午膳 Lunch
点菜 à la carte ￥60-100
晚膳 Dinner
点菜 à la carte ￥60-100

■ 营业时间 **OPENING HOURS**
午膳 lunch 11:00-14:00 (L.O.)
晚膳 Dinner 17:00-21:00 (L.O.)

😃

蜀三味 · 川菜（闵行） N

SHUM SAM WEI (MINHANG)

川菜 · 朴实

Sichuan · Rustic

"古蜀有三国，川菜有三味"正是餐厅名字的由来，餐厅遵循古法烹调，务求还原巴蜀风味，主要食材如郫县豆瓣酱均从四川运到。餐单选择多且价钱亲民，招牌菜包括川辣古法水煮鱼，厨师将之减少油分，并降低辣度；而配上四川油醋汁的秘制小排骨略带西式风味；最后不妨一尝以泉水制造的甜品冰粉。

This is the first branch of this three-store chain in Shanghai. The interior features plenty of wood and bamboo, imitating rustic Sichuan architecture. Diners have plenty of choice and prices are fair. The signature boiled fish fillet in chilli oil can be tailored to your preferred spiciness. Spare ribs are marinated in barbecue sauce with vinaigrette to cut through the fattiness.

大蔬无界（徐汇）
WUJIE (XUHUI)

素食·简约

Vegetarian · Minimalist

此家店子是品牌旗下首家食店，正对徐家汇公园，占地五层，室内布置以中国五行原理揉合现代设计理念，风格独特。餐厅供应的素菜以传统养生饮食哲学为基础，选用最新鲜当造的食材、运用国际化的烹调手法制作，有创意且口味清新，带给你不一样的素食体验。店家设下午茶套餐及套餐，建议提前预订。

The original branch of the Wujie vegetarian restaurants occupies a five storey building facing the lush greenery of Xujiahui Park. Its décor blends the five elements of Chinese philosophy with modern design. You can expect the same carefully prepared vegetarian dishes as in their other branches, which are strong on presentation and not without the occasional surprise in flavour. Tea set menus are also available.

⚭14 ◎🍴
TEL. 3469 2857
徐汇区天平路392号
392 Tianping Road, Xuhui

■ 价钱 PRICE
点菜 à la carte ¥ 180-220

■ 营业时间 OPENING HOURS
11:00-22:00 (L.O.)

徐汇及闵行区 XUHUI & MINHANG

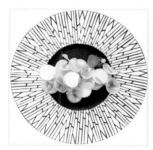

P ⇆ 22 ◔⏰

TEL. 6427 2233

徐汇区漕溪北路201号
201 North Caoxi Road, Xuhui

■ **价钱 PRICE**
午膳 Lunch
点菜 à la carte ¥ 150-250
晚膳 Dinner
点菜 à la carte ¥ 150-250

■ **营业时间 OPENING HOURS**
午膳 Lunch 11:00-14:00 (L.O.)
晚膳 Dinner 17:00-22:00 (L.O.)

■ **休息日期 ANNUAL AND WEEKLY CLOSING**
农历新年休息4天
Closed 4 days Lunar New Year

🐶

上海老站
YE OLDE STATION

沪菜·经典

Shanghainese · Classic décor

踏入怀旧气息浓浓的上海老站,仿如置身二、三十年代的老上海之中,再往里走,坐进后园草坪上两节由旧火车车厢改装而成的餐室,更有时光倒流之感。曾用作慈禧和宋庆龄专用车厢的餐室固然难得一见,叫食客一再光临的却是做法正宗的一道道上海本帮菜,红烧回鱼、虾籽乌参等都叫人再三回味。

A palpable sense of history hits you as soon as you enter this restaurant – and that's even before you've spotted the two hundred-year old converted train carriages that are sitting in the garden. Don't, however, think customers keep coming back because this is some sort of museum piece – they are really here for the Shanghainese cuisine. Stand-outs include the braised fish and stewed sea cucumber with shrimp roe.

麦德龙邀您开启
安心高品质购物体验

一站式购齐 买更多价更低

　　麦德龙提供近25,000种商品，及不同大小包装。无论是专业人士，还是吃货、达人，都满足你的所需。

　　优享会会员更可全年享受3件95折、精选商品6件最低8折，还有积分换好礼！

高品质食材 呵护安心生活

　　麦德龙旗下麦咨达可追溯系统、HACCP国际食品安全保证体系和全程冷链运输，为食材提供安全可靠的品质保障。新鲜安全、品种丰富，高品质的食材，呵护你的安心生活。

全球精选 彰显不凡品味

　　麦德龙精选4,000多种进口商品，高品质的牛肉、冰鲜三文鱼及冻品海鲜；专业大师品鉴的葡萄酒；蕴含丰富营养的五谷杂粮；符合食品安全规范的优质器皿等。全球直采，高性价比，为你的生活增添不凡品味。

启发灵感 烹调美味人生

　　麦德龙互动坊开设专业烹饪培训。麦德龙厨房定期发布激发灵感的食谱。关注麦德龙中国微信，第一时间了解"美酒大咖"及"美厨课堂"的最新动态。

麦德龙中国微信

下载麦德龙中国APP

广告

AKMÉ

时尚法国菜·时尚
French contemporary · Contemporary décor

餐厅隐身于公园一幢百岁历史建筑内，入口处宏伟的雕饰天花和古式古香的窗户让人不期然驻足欣赏。走到尽处向左拐就是餐厅所在。圆形餐桌铺上白色桌布，配以丝绒座椅，含蓄而富格调。厨房以玻璃墙分隔，可窥见厨师在内大显身手。餐单提供四至八道菜的法国佳肴，顾问厨师的餐厅遍佈各地，水准毋庸置疑。

Contemporary French cuisine in a tastefully remodeled building circa 1910s in the former French Concession sounds like a great idea. Renowned French-Algerian chef Akrame Benallal embraced the concept with AKMé featuring high sculpted ceilings, arched French windows, slick minimalist furniture and a glass-clad wine cellar. During the day, tapas is served in the salon and the lush garden. Prix-fixe fine-dining menus only at night.

♿ 🅿 👥20 🍴 🍷

TEL. 6469 9969

徐汇区乌鲁木齐南路55号
55 South Wulumuqi Road, Xuhui

■ 价钱 **PRICE**
晚膳 Dinner
套餐 set ¥ 588-1,288
点菜 à la carte ¥ 450-650

■ 营业时间 **OPENING HOURS**
晚膳 Dinner 18:00-22:00 (L.O.)

徐汇及闵行区 XUHUI & MINHANG

🏠 ← 🍽 🅿 ⊙🍴 ⚙

TEL. 8011 9999

闵行区元江路6161弄
6161 Yuanjiang Road, Minhang
www.aman.com/shanghai

■ 价钱 **PRICE**
午膳 Lunch
点菜 à la carte ¥ 400-1,000
晚膳 Dinner
点菜 à la carte ¥ 400-1,000

■ 营业时间 **OPENING HOURS**
午膳 lunch 12:00-14:30 (L.O.)
晚膳 Dinner 18:00-22:00 (L.O.)

ARVA N

意大利菜 · 典雅
Italian · Elegant

方形的餐室透过落地玻璃采纳大量自然光，天花以金丝楠木作装饰，格调优雅。主厨烹调意大利菜经验老到，选材新鲜、符合季节是其烹调宗旨，除运用本地蔬菜和来自世界各地的食材，更在餐厅自设小型蔬果园。自设饼房每天出炉的糕点和面包素质上乘。自家制意大利云吞和席前炮制的提拉米苏都不容错过。餐厅保安严密，必须订座。

This restaurant in a luxury resort away from the city champions a farm-to-table concept with its own vegetable garden. The experienced chef is passionate about food and he cooks quality ingredients à la minute. Homemade ravioli and tiramisu are not to be missed. The airy, elegant dining room and the friendly, professional manager also add to the experience. Reservations mandatory; a security check is undertaken at the hotel entrance.

古铜法式餐厅
CUIVRE

时尚法国菜·型格
French contemporary· Design

一家开在法国领事馆旧址上的法国餐厅，到此用餐的多是生意人和熟客。以木制家具、木柱、木吊灯塑造出温暖宁静的氛围，吧台前自行车形状的高椅，带点法国风情。鹅肝酱、卷心菜叶包香煎鹅肝、油焖鸭腿和猪脚均不能错过。

Idiosyncratic design touches, like bar seats fashioned from bicycles, add personality to this always welcoming bistro in the French Concession. Must-try dishes are poached foie gras marinated in port wine, and 'Crépinette' of foie gras, duck leg confit and trotter.

P ☺️🍴 ⛸

TEL. 6437 4219
徐汇区淮海中路1502号
1502 Middle Huaihai Road, Xuhui

■ **价钱 PRICE**
周末早午拼餐 Weekend brunch
套餐 set ￥198-314
晚膳 Dinner
点菜 à la carte ￥300-400

■ **营业时间 OPENING HOURS**
周末早午拼餐 Weekend brunch
12:00-14:00 (L.O.)
晚膳 Dinner 18:00-22:00 (L.O.)

■ **休息日期 ANNUAL AND WEEKLY CLOSING**
农历新年14天及周二休息
Closed 14 days Lunar New Year and Tuesday

徐汇及闵行区 **XUHUI & MINHANG**

👤🏠♨️ P ⟷24 🍴

TEL. 6472 9778

徐汇区宛平路290号徐家汇公园内

Xujiahui Park, 290 Wanping Road, Xuhui

■ 价钱 PRICE

午膳 Lunch
点菜 à la carte ¥ 200-350
晚膳 Dinner
点菜 à la carte ¥ 300-500

■ 营业时间 OPENING HOURS

11:00-21:45 (L.O.)

🍴⚪

恒悦轩（徐汇）

HANG YUEN HIN (XUHUI)

粤菜·典雅

Cantonese · Elegant

恒悦轩的总店于2005年在徐家汇公园里开业，舒适的环境加上园林景色，在此用餐确是赏心乐事。餐厅主理高级粤菜，主厨曾于粤港两地工作，融汇两地饮食文化，炮制出少油少盐、保持食材原味又有益健康的菜肴。此店的招牌菜式不少，西杏炸虾卷和木瓜椰奶炖燕窝均值得试试。

Here at the original Hang Yuen Hin, which opened in 2005, the greenery of the park outside the windows combines with a comfortable dining room to create a relaxing and enjoyable experience. The chef has worked in both Guangzhou and Hong Kong; know-how which he puts to good use in his Cantonese cuisine – his food is also low in salt and oil. Signature dishes include fried shrimp with almond, and double-boiled bird's nest with coconut milk.

鮨 大山
SUSHI OYAMA

寿司·典雅
Sushi · Elegant

餐厅在2009年开业，装潢简约。主厨大山师傅每天都带着相同的热情和执着，按着当天新鲜从北海道和长崎空运到的食材设计菜单，不论是刺身材料的素质还是寿司饭的烹调，也力求做到尽善尽美。建议预订座位时选择能欣赏厨师准备食物、只有十个的寿司柜台座位。

You'll need to pay attention when you get to the second floor because the entrance to this little sushi restaurant is not only tiny but also hidden. The place is run by a friendly Japanese chef and has just 10 seats at a counter, so booking is strongly advised. He delivers a set menu using ingredients imported mostly from Hokkaido and Nagasaki and not only pays attention to the quality of the fish, but also to the rice and vinegar.

🪑10 🚗 ⊘🍴
TEL. 5404 7705
徐汇区东湖路20号2楼
2F, 20 Donghu Road, Xuhui
www.fulufamily.com

■ 价钱 **PRICE**
晚膳 Dinner
套餐 set ￥1,280

■ 营业时间 **OPENING HOURS**
晚膳 Dinner 18:30-21:00 (L.O.)

■ 休息日期 **ANNUAL AND WEEKLY CLOSING**
中国传统节日及周日休息
Closed Chinese traditional festivals and Sunday

徐汇及闵行区 XUHUI & MINHANG

P ⊘💶

TEL. 6437 9633

徐汇区淮海中路1502号2楼

2F, 1502 Middle Huaihai Road, Xuhui

■ 价钱 **PRICE**

午膳 Lunch
套餐 set ¥ 148
点菜 à la carte ¥ 150-400
晚膳 Dinner
点菜 à la carte ¥ 150-400

■ 营业时间 **OPENING HOURS**

周末早午拼餐 Weekend brunch
12:00-14:00 (L.O.)
晚膳 Dinner 18:00-22:00 (L.O.)

■ 休息日期 **ANNUAL AND WEEKLY CLOSING**

农历新年14天及周二休息
Closed 14 days Lunar New Year and Tuesday

🍴🍽

T FOR THAI

泰国菜·时尚

Thai · Contemporary décor

餐厅巧妙地将竹、木、皮革、铜和植物等元素混合，令餐室环境舒适而富特色。主厨Michael同时主理法国餐厅Cuivre，他在曼谷跟朋友深造泰国菜的技巧，并把所学带到这餐厅，配上新鲜食材，呈献出叫人再三回味的泰国菜肴。每逢周六、日的早午拼餐时段设有小童区，适合一家大小欢聚。

The team behind Cuivre has created a warm and colourful Thai restaurant with touches of whimsy in its look; to the side is a green hued bar. Michael learned to cook Thai food in Bangkok; his menu is affordable and appealing and the flavours of his dishes are balanced and nuanced. It's family time at weekends when brunch is provided and a corner of the room becomes a kids' zone.

牛排薯条色拉

THE CUT

扒房·时尚

Steakhouse · Contemporary décor

餐单一如餐厅名称般简单直接，这扒房以原产澳洲的谷饲安格斯牛为主，虽然餐牌简单，佐膳的配料一点也不马虎，每款牛扒分别配以黄油酱、烧烤酱和阿根廷酱三种酱汁，另有四款别有特色的盐和两款芥末。自助色拉吧无限量供应色拉。嗜酒人士不妨试试酒吧提供的鸡尾酒。

There's a lot to be said for restaurants incorporating their speciality into the name of the restaurant – while there are dishes like burgers and roast chicken on the menu at this bright and lively spot, you know that everyone is really here for the beef. After you've had your fill of the salad bar, you can treat yourself with Australian grass-fed Black Angus, and add one of the three sauces.

TEL. 6443 5136

徐汇区淮海中路999号
环贸广场6楼606

L6-606, iapm,
999 Middle Huaihai Road, Xuhui

www.thecut-shanghai.com

■ 价钱 **PRICE**
午膳 Lunch
套餐 set ￥68-158
点菜 à la carte ￥220-500
晚膳 Dinner
点菜 à la carte ￥300-600

■ 营业时间 **OPENING HOURS**
11:00-22:30 (L.O.)

徐汇及闵行区 XUHUI & MINHANG

HOTELS
酒店

养云安缦

AMANYANGYUN

豪华·古典

Luxury · Historic

养云安缦于2018年开幕，酒店建筑是由江西迁移修复的明清古代庭院，金丝楠木、河北黑石材与竹子相互搭配的设计贯穿各处空间，饶有古意。酒店设套房及独立别墅，各房间均设有两个小庭院，住客可在庭院浴缸内享受私密的户外沐浴体验，尽情放松身心。餐膳选择涵盖中西口味，更可参与诸如书法、品茗、调香等艺康体活动。

An hour away from the city is this luxury resort hotel, which opened in 2018. It boasts Ming and Qing dynasty houses and a historic camphor tree relocated from Jiangxi and carefully replanted. Its 24 courtyard suites and 13 walled villas are tastefully furnished with nammu wood, black stones and bamboo. There is an Italian, a Japanese and a Chinese restaurant and activities include calligraphy classes and yoga.

TEL. 8011 9999

闵行区元江路6161弄
6161 Yuanjiang Road, Minhang
www.aman.com/shanghai

24 客房/**Rooms**
13 套房/**Suites**

套房价格/**Price for suites:**
¥ 6,000-6,500

餐厅推荐/**Recommended restaurants:**
Arva ⭑○

TEL. 5466 6688

徐汇区建国西路480号

480 West Jianguo Road, Xuhui

www.capellashanghai.com

55 套房/Suites

套房价格/Price for suites:
¥ 2,000-4,000

餐厅推荐/Recommended restaurants:
Le Comptoir de Pierre Gagnaire ❄

建业里嘉佩乐

CAPELLA JIAN YE LI

豪华 · 型格

Luxury · Design

上海昔日规模最大的石库门清水红砖建筑群，修缮后于2017年改建为酒店，55个房间均为套房，其中五间位处于两层高独立屋内，更是豪华。客房均以法国家具搭配墙上的中国画作，时尚别致。庭园内古雅的水塔是酒店地标，入夜后会改变颜色，甚为壮观。欲肆意歇息，不妨到访全新的水疗及桑拿设施。

Historic stone-gate alleyways were carefully restored to house this hidden gem with its villas that marry modern French décor with smart Chinese accents and artwork. The architectural highlight, a water tower in a courtyard, is lit in varying colours at night. After a day of busy sightseeing or work, you can wind down at the spa. Attentive service is another plus here.

© 2017 Sui Sicong, All Rights Reserved / Amanyangyun

徐汇及闵行区 **XUHUI & MINHANG**

W. Kaehler/age fotostock

虹口区
HONGKOU

RESTAURANTS
餐厅

🍴○

新大陆－中国厨房
XINDALU - CHINA KITCHEN

沪菜·时尚

Shanghainese • Contemporary décor

开放式的厨房内，全神贯注且忙碌地烹调食材的厨师团队，在众目睽睽的情况下为食客预备美味佳肴，为确保阁下能欣赏到精湛的烹饪示范，不妨要求靠近厨房位置的餐桌。餐牌主要由沪菜和江浙菜组成，但北京果木烤鸭也是其招牌菜，欲品尝务必要尽早到达餐馆。

This restaurant within the Hyatt features a fantastic open kitchen, so make sure you ask for a table close by in order to watch the chefs at work. Shanghainese dishes make up the core of the extensive menu; Jiang Zhe dishes are something the kitchen here does very well but its speciality is Peking duck – the ducks are cooked in the wood oven and so it's well worth arriving early to order one.

 ♿ 🅿 ⟷10 ◐🍴

TEL. 6393 1234

虹口区黄浦路199号
外滩茂悦大酒店

**Hyatt on The Bund,
199 Huangpu Road, Hongkou**

shanghaithebund.hyatt.com

■ 价钱 **PRICE**
午膳 Lunch
点菜 à la carte ￥210-825
晚膳 Dinner
点菜 à la carte ￥210-825

■ 营业时间 **OPENING HOURS**
午膳 Lunch 11:30-14:30 (L.O.)
晚膳 Dinner 17:30-22:30 (L.O.)

虹口区 **HONGKOU**

虹口区 HONGKOU

 ♿ 🅿 ⇔12 🚇 ☺🍴

TEL. 6537 5939

虹口区高阳路168号
外滩浦华大酒店5楼

**5F, Sunrise on the Bund,
168 Gaoyang Road, Hongkou**

www.sunrisesha.com

■ 价钱 PRICE
午膳 Lunch
套餐 set ¥ 198-398
点菜 à la carte ¥ 230-1,170
晚膳 Dinner
套餐 set ¥ 588-2,280
点菜 à la carte ¥ 230-1,170

■ 营业时间 OPENING HOURS
午膳 Lunch 11:30-13:30 (L.O.)
晚膳 Dinner 17:30-21:00 (L.O.)

🍴

讚
ZAN

铁板烧・传统
Teppanyaki・Traditional

掌厨的台湾厨师有逾二十年烹调经验，他利用新鲜菜蔬及进口自台湾澎湖的海鲜，配以各种酱汁和精美摆盘，让食客尝到不一样的铁板烧。除了菜牌上的套餐，亦可选择厨师发办，不妨于订座时提出。外脆内软的半熟生蚝及肉汁淋漓的和牛是厨师得意之作。餐室开扬，另设三间私密度高的厢房。

With over 20 years of experience on the teppanyaki grill, the Taiwanese head chef perfected his art by the bold use of sauces, transforming seafood from Penghu, quality meat and veggies into palatable art on the spot. Succulent oysters with crispy skin, and seared Wagyu beef bursting with juices are not to be missed. Pick from set menus or order omakase-style. General seating in the dining hall aside, three private rooms are available.

PamelaJoeMcFarlane/iStock

虹口区 **HONGKOU**

虹口区 **HONGKOU**

HOTELS
酒店

悦榕庄

BANYAN TREE

水疗・豪华

Spa and wellness・Luxury

酒店坐落在外滩北边，与国际邮轮码头相距不远。时尚豪华的装潢，全部房间都能观赏黄浦江或陆家嘴商业区景色，自然深受住客爱戴。大型双人床、完备的设施、宽敞的浴室、含亚洲风的时尚典雅布置，让身心尽情放松。巨型泳池、舒适的水疗中心和设备完善的健身房，带给你不一样的体验。

The bedrooms at this urban retreat on the north part of the Bund are bigger than most and are stylishly decorated, with subtle Asian influences and modern art. The bathrooms are particularly impressive; their large windows allow natural light to flood in. The hotel is all about rest and relaxation so naturally there is also a pleasant spa and a large swimming pool.

TEL. 2509 1188

虹口区公平路19号
19 Gongping Road, Hongkou

www.banyantree.com/zh/china/ shanghai-on-the-bund

106 客房/**Rooms**
24 套房/**Suites**
双人房价格/**Price for 2 persons:**
¥ 2,210-4,660

TEL. 6393 1234
虹口区黄浦路199号
199 Huangpu Road, Hongkou
shanghaithebund.hyatt.com

572 客房/**Rooms**
48 套房/**Suites**

双人房价格/**Price for 2 persons:**
¥ 1,800-2,400

餐厅推荐/**Recommended restaurants:**
新大陆 - 中国厨房 Xindalu - China
Kitchen

外滩茂悦
HYATT ON THE BUND

商务・时尚
Business・Contemporary

华丽的大堂内,一道清澈的河流,仿若浮华人间中的一股清泉,瞬间扣住了紊乱的心思。然而,更叫人屏息的,是32楼非常时髦酒吧的窗外景致。分布于两座高塔内的客房,时尚雅致,更能欣赏到悠悠黄浦江之景。要让身心灵得到片刻安舒,源Spa水疗中心的服务定能使你如愿。

The expansive lobby and its water feature are bound to impress – as will the breathtaking views from the VUE bar on the 32nd floor. Split between two towers, the bedrooms offer contemporary comforts as well as views of the river. There are plenty of dining options, from dim sum to European specialities. Yuan Spa offers a range of treatments for the weary.

外滩浦华

SUNRISE ON THE BUND

商务 · 经典

Business · Classic

坐落于魔都最引人入胜的黄浦外滩上，与外滩游船码头相距不远的上海外滩浦华大酒店，不论是购物、游览或公干皆相宜。酒店装潢高贵典雅，大堂天花上的巨幅彩色玻璃不经意地震撼着住客的心神。古典的房间布置，感觉舒适。逛得累了，不妨到老船长酒吧尝尝以古老的德国酿酒方法酿制的啤酒。

Close to the cruise ship terminal sits this well-managed hotel boasting the largest collection of stained glass in the city – the lobby ceiling is particularly impressive. Dining options include Taiwanese seafood and Japanese, while the Old Captain bar does a good impression of a characterful pub and brews its own beer. Bedrooms are classic in style.

虹口区 HONGKOU

TEL. 5558 9999

虹口区高阳路168号

168 Gaoyang Road, Hongkou

www.sunrisesha.com

143 客房/**Rooms**
13 套房/**Suites**

双人房价格/**Price for 2 persons:**
¥ 898-3,280

餐厅推荐/**Recommended restaurants:**
讚 Zan

TEL. 2286 9999
虹口区旅顺路66号
66 Lushun Road, Hongkou
www.whotels.com/shanghaithebund

339 客房/**Rooms**
35 套房/**Suites**
双人房价格/**Price for 2 persons:**
￥ 2,300-4,700

W

豪华·艺术

Luxury · Art déco

酒店风格时尚，以红白色为主调，四周陈设了不少当代
艺术家的作品。透明电梯从地下贯通大堂，旁边悬挂
着以霓虹灯组成的上海古今地标名称，住客可细味魔
都演变。客房贯彻集团大胆创新的风格，每個房間均
摆放了代表上海的巨型筷子及小笼包坐垫，并设有情
境灯，可按喜好转换颜色。切记到户外泳池玩乐一番。

The red and white neon signs surrounding the
glass-clad lifts to the lobby feel clubby and
fun. Rooms follow the same colour scheme and
most have river views. In line with the cheeky
image of the brand, chopstick and Xiao long
bao pillows are put on the bed to remind you
which city you are in. The outdoor pool with
the stunning Pudong skyline will wash the
stress away.

© Limelight Studio / Banyan Tree

虹口区 **HONGKOU**

aiqingwang/iStock

浦东新区

PUDONG

浦东新区 **PUDONG**

RESTAURANTS
餐厅

苏浙总会
JADE MANSION

淮扬菜 · 典雅

Huai Yang · Elegant

苏浙总会与苏浙汇同出一门，但定位更为高档，设在上海其中一个顶级商场国金中心内，位置可说是便利之至。装潢时尚而富格调的餐厅分成几个小区，各区自成一角，宁静舒适。这儿提供新派淮扬菜，部分菜式更加入国际化食材，外观摩登又讨好，尽显厨师巧思。

The group behind Jardin de Jade created Jade Mansion as their premier brand. Sitting in the city's most exclusive mall, it comes divided into different sections, is stylishly decorated and considerably less noisy than many restaurants. The menu offers diners the chance to experience many Huai Yang dishes, which use some international ingredients, come with the occasional modern twist and arrive beautifully presented.

P ⇆20 ⓞ🍴

TEL. 5012 7728

浦东新区世纪大道8号
国金中心商场4楼13号铺

**L4-13, Shanghai IFC Mall,
8 Century Avenue, Pudong**

www.jade388.com

■ 价钱 **PRICE**
午膳 Lunch
点菜 à la carte ¥ 250-500
晚膳 Dinner
点菜 à la carte ¥ 300-500

■ 营业时间 **OPENING HOURS**
午膳 Lunch 11:00-16:00 (L.O.)
晚膳 Dinner 17:00-22:30 (L.O.)

浦东新区 **PUDONG**

195

浦东新区 PUDONG

🅿 ⇔16 ◎🍴

TEL. 5106 1688

浦东新区世纪大道8号
国金中心商场3楼17-18号

**L3-17 & 18, Shanghai IFC Mall,
8 Century Avenue, Pudong**

■ 价钱 PRICE
午膳 Lunch
点菜 à la carte ￥150-500
晚膳 Dinner
点菜 à la carte ￥250-500

■ 营业时间 OPENING HOURS
午膳 Lunch 11:30-14:30 (L.O.)
晚膳 Dinner 17:30-21:30 (L.O)

🌸

利苑（浦东新区）
LEI GARDEN (PUDONG)

粤菜 · 时尚

Cantonese · Contemporary décor

国金中心内的利苑酒家总是座无虚席，概因高素质的粤菜大家都爱吃。老火汤和精制广东点心是午饭时段上班族的最爱。晚饭时间，你可以从主菜单点选海鲜、鱼肚等高级食品，亦可从特别菜单中点选时令小炒或煲仔菜等等。无论中午还是晚上，都必须预早订座。

Reservations are a must as this Lei Garden in IFC is continuously packed with people craving good quality Cantonese cuisine. At lunchtime, customers come in droves for the expertly crafted dim sum and the soups. The dinner menu offers premium dishes like seafood and dried fish maw. Those wishing to avoid making too much of a dent in their wallets should opt for the seasonal stir-fries and casseroles.

迷上海
SHANG-HIGH CUISINE

沪菜·经典

Shanghainese · Classic

餐厅位于设计独特的卓美亚喜玛拉雅酒店内，深木镶板、大理石地面及特色灯光交织出典雅时尚的用餐环境，餐单却以经典的上海菜肴为主，在传统名菜的基础上进行创新改良，提升至另一层次。不论是老上海三黄鸡或目鱼红烧肉，味道均恰到好处，显尽厨师超凡的厨艺。

On the sixth floor of the Jumeirah hotel is this stylish restaurant with a marble floor, attractive lighting and dark wood panelling. In contrast to the room's modern look, the menu offers a classic style of Shanghainese cuisine. Dishes are expertly crafted and elevated to a new level, thanks to occasional use of modern techniques. Try the 'San Huang' chicken and braised pork belly with cuttlefish to fully experience the precision of the cooking.

& P ⟷20 ©⁐

TEL. 3858 0768

浦东新区梅花路1108号
卓美亚喜玛拉雅酒店6楼

**6F, Jumeirah Himalayas Hotel,
1108 Mei Hua Road, Pudong**

www.jumeirah.com

■ 价钱 **PRICE**
午膳 Lunch
点菜 à la carte ¥ 200-300
晚膳 Dinner
点菜 à la carte ¥ 300-400

■ 营业时间 **OPENING HOURS**
午膳 Lunch 11:30-14:15 (L.O.)
晚膳 Dinner 17:30-22:15 (L.O.)

浦东新区 **PUDONG**

👤 ⛩ 🛁 🅿️ 🔌60 🔳

TEL. 2082 9888

浦东新区浦东南路111号
浦东文华东方酒店LG

**LG, Mandarin Oriental Pudong,
111 South Pudong Road, Pudong**

**www.mandarinoriental.com/
shanghai**

■ **价钱 PRICE**
午膳 Lunch
点菜 à la carte ¥ 240-1,090
晚膳 Dinner
点菜 à la carte ¥ 240-1,090

■ **营业时间 OPENING HOURS**
午膳 Lunch 11:30-14:30 (L.O.)
晚膳 Dinner 17:30-22:30 (L.O.)

雍颐庭
YONG YI TING

沪菜・经典
Shanghainese・Classic

雍颐庭以供应经典江南菜见称，菜式不但卖相精美，且味道掌握得恰到好处，其中红炖蟹肉狮子头令人印象深刻，以熏鲳鱼作为前菜也是蛮不错的选择。布置得赏心悦目的大堂、挂满整个天花的中式吊灯、镶有龙图屏风的卡座、迷人的水池，食物未尝，已先在视觉上得到满足。

It may be located beneath the hotel but this tastefully decorated restaurant comes with a charming water terrace. Its decoration is influenced by modern Chinese styles – the booths with their curtains and dragon motifs are particularly charming. The well-known chef delivers classics from the surrounding Jiang Nan region. Look out for the Lion's Head pork dumpling with crab meat in sweet soy sauce.

正斗粥面专家（浦东新区）

TASTY CONGEE & NOODLE WANTUN SHOP (PUDONG)

粥面・东方
Noodles and Congee • Oriental décor

餐厅自2010年开业，至今已有八年，与在香港的总店一样，以提供高素质云吞面和粥品见称，当然也有供应其他港式美食。位处国际金融中心，收取平民价钱，晚饭时段自然非常繁忙。大多数本地食客均是为了品尝一下香港云吞面的特色而来。

Anyone who knows Hong Kong will be familiar with the Tasty group of restaurants and may well have spent time queuing in front of one in readiness for a bowl of their wonton noodles. This branch in IFC opened in 2010 and shares the same level of popularity – especially at dinner – with its many fans hankering for their Hong Kong style wonton noodles, congee and other reasonably priced dishes.

TEL. 5012 3998

浦东新区世纪大道8号
国金中心商场3楼9号铺
**L3-9, Shanghai IFC Mall,
8 Century Avenue, Pudong**
www.tasty.com.hk

■ 价钱 PRICE
午膳 Lunch
点菜 à la carte ¥ 110-150

■ 营业时间 OPENING HOURS
11:00-21:30 (L.O.)

浦东新区 PUDONG

P ⟷12 ⓞ🍴

TEL. 6877 7716

浦东新区世纪大道100号
环球金融中心3楼308-309

308-309, 3F,
Shanghai World Financial Centre,
100 Century Avenue, Pudong

■ 价钱 **PRICE**
点菜 à la carte ¥ 180-220

■ 营业时间 **OPENING HOURS**
11:00-21:00 (L.O.)

😋

大蔬无界（浦东新区）
WUJIE (PUDONG)

素食・时尚

Vegetarian・Contemporary décor

大蔬无界在上海有数家分店，集团期盼打破宗教、国
界之限，以丰富多变的菜式，令素食变得更为普及，
故取名"無界"。其菜单善用时令食材，不但随季节
时有变化，且融入中国传统养生文化，烹调方法不拘
泥于某地域或菜系，灵活多变，外观既新颖且破格，
惊喜处处。浦东这家分店有较多带和风的菜式。

Its name means 'without borders' and that
reflects the owner's take on vegetarian cooking –
international flavours from across all religious and
geographical boundaries. Seasonal ingredients
are transformed with modern techniques while
encompassing Chinese healthy dietary concepts.
Creativity is also evident in the exquisite
presentation. This branch also offers dishes with
pronounced Japanese influences.

全日

CAMELIA

意大利菜·时尚

Italian · Contemporary décor

以供应意大利菜为主的全日，大厨在选料上非常用心严谨，大部分食材均由意大利进口，再经过他精心处理，每道菜式都色香味俱全。招牌菜包括茄子节瓜千层塔及风干火腿披萨配芝麻生菜等。晚餐时段，除了零点菜单外，还有品尝套餐可供选择。

A high ceiling, low level lighting, dark marble flooring and huge windows help make this Italian restaurant at the Four Seasons feel both comfortable and intimate. The chef pays heed to the quality of the ingredients, which he mostly imports from Italy, and the open kitchen allows customers to watch his team prepare the flavoursome dishes. Highlights include spaghetti with clams and sea urchin; veal Milanese; and eggplant and zucchini parmigiana.

TEL. 2036 1300

浦东新区世纪大道210号
浦东四季酒店1楼

**1F, Four Seasons Pudong,
210 Century Avenue, Pudong**

www.fourseasons.com/pudong

■ 价钱 PRICE
午膳 Lunch
套餐 set ¥ 300-600
点菜 à la carte ¥ 290-660
晚膳 Dinner
套餐 set ¥ 400-500
点菜 à la carte ¥ 290-660

■ 营业时间 OPENING HOURS
午膳 Lunch 11:30-14:30 (L.O.)
周日午膳 Sunday lunch
11:45-15:00 (L.O.)
晚膳 Dinner 17:30-21:45 (L.O.)

浦东新区 **PUDONG**

P ⟳48 ◖ⅈ

TEL. 6880 9778

浦东新区世纪大道201号
渣打银行大厦3-4楼

**3-4F, Standard Chartered Tower,
201 Century Avenue, Pudong**

■ 价钱 **PRICE**
午膳 Lunch
点菜 à la carte ¥ 150-350
晚膳 Dinner
点菜 à la carte ¥ 200-500

■ 营业时间 **OPENING HOURS**
午膳 Lunch 11:00-14:30 (L.O.)
晚膳 Dinner 18:00-21:30 (L.O.)

🍴◯

恒悦轩（浦东新区）
HANG YUEN HIN (PUDONG)

粤菜 · 时尚

Cantonese · Contemporary décor

恒悦轩在上海市区有两家分店，都是做精致港式粤
菜，总厨融汇粤港两地之精髓，选用新鲜时令食材，
炮制出少油少盐、保持食材原味又有益健康的菜肴。
中午时可以享用港式点心和汤品，晚上可试试清蒸海
鲜或金蒜蒸小青龙虾。此店在2009年开业，中午时
段颇繁忙，订座时可同时预留食物如例汤和烧味等。

This sister to the original branch opened in
2009 and provides a similarly healthy range of
carefully prepared Cantonese dishes. It gets
particularly busy at lunchtime thanks largely to
the quality of the dim sum and soups – these
soups, as well as the roast meats, can be pre-
ordered when you reserve a table. At dinner,
it's dishes like steamed seafood and abalone
which prove popular.

金轩

JIN XUAN

粤菜 · 豪华

Cantonese · Luxury

位于浦东丽思卡尔顿53楼的金轩，由拥有逾十年粤菜经验的厨师主理，以高素质的食材制作出色香味皆优的美食。招牌菜包括黄金燕麦龙虾球等。餐厅的一系列茶饮尤为出色。曾是经验侍酒师的餐厅经理可替你搭配餐酒与佳肴。

The head chef brings the considerable experience he garnered at some famous Cantonese restaurants in Hong Kong to bear at this elegant restaurant on the 53rd floor of the Ritz-Carlton. The wine list is impressive, as is the selection of teas. The views are a given and the room itself is very comfortable and well run.

🅟 ⇆30

TEL. 2020 1717

浦东新区世纪大道8号
丽思卡尔顿酒店53楼

**53F, The Ritz-Carlton Pudong,
8 Century Avenue, Pudong**

www.ritzcarlton.cn/shanghaipudong

■ 价钱 **PRICE**

午膳 Lunch
套餐 set ¥ 230-400
点菜 à la carte ¥ 230-1,000
晚膳 Dinner
套餐 set ¥ 880-1,680
点菜 à la carte ¥ 230-1,000

■ 营业时间 **OPENING HOURS**
午膳 Lunch 11:30-13:45 (L.O.)
晚膳 Dinner 17:30-22:00 (L.O.)

浦东新区 **PUDONG**

 🅿 ⇌16 🍴

TEL. 5012 0637

浦东新区世纪大道8号
国金中心商场4楼

**4F, Shanghai IFC Mall,
8 Century Avenue, Pudong**

■ 价钱 **PRICE**
点菜 à la carte ¥ 200-500

■ 营业时间 **OPENING HOURS**
11:00-21:30 (L.O.)

🍴

兰·俏江南（国金中心）
LAN SOUTH BEAUTY (IFC)

川菜·友善
Sichuan · Friendly

2000年在北京开业的俏江南，发展至今旗下食店已
遍布全国二十多个城市。国金中心的这家分店在店名
前冠上兰字，是集团内的高级食店。亮丽而现代的装
潢，与新派川菜搭配得宜。最好相约亲友共享大锅的
极品毛血旺或是堂煮的江石滚肥牛，其肉香在两丈以
外也能嗅到。店内设酒吧区和包厢。

The South Beauty group opened their first
branch in Beijing in 2000 and since then have
expanded into more than 20 cities. This is their
high-end restaurant – 'Lan' means 'orchid' – and
its modern look is a good match for the Sichuan
cooking which comes with contemporary twists.
Don't miss the wonderfully spicy stewed ox tripe
and duck blood curd, which is best shared with
friends, or the scalded beef on hot stone, which
is prepared by your table.

🍴

莱美露滋

MAISON LAMELOISE

时尚法国菜·亲密

French contemporary · Intimate

高踞新开幕的商业大楼68层，食客可在外滩美景的180度环抱下品尝美食。曾在法籍厨师Éric Pras麾下工作多年的主厨把最正宗的法国菜从勃艮第带来上海，分量亦与法国总店同样丰富。餐单上也有揉合欧亚风味的菜式；餐单按季节更换，鹌鹑蛋红酒干葱奶油冷汤及鳌虾叫人再三回味。

The first Asian outpost of its namesake in Burgundy is on the 68th floor of the city's latest landmark and boasts 180-degree views of The Bund. The chef has worked for Éric Pras at the flagship for years and is keen to re-create an authentic Burgundian experience with delicate flavours and generous portion sizes. Culinary highlights such as quail with meurette custard cream and duo of langoustine are masterfully executed.

♿ ≺ 🅿 ⊙🍴

TEL. 6881 6789

浦东新区银城中路501号
上海中心大厦68楼

68F, Shanghai Tower,
501 Middle Yincheng Road, Pudong

www.lameloise.com.cn

■ 价钱 **PRICE**
午膳 Lunch
套餐 set ¥ 488-1,688
晚膳 Dinner
套餐 set ¥ 2,088-2,588

■ 营业时间 **OPENING HOURS**
午膳 Lunch 11:30-13:30 (L.O.)
晚膳 Dinner 18:00-21:00 (L.O.)

■ 休息日期 **ANNUAL AND WEEKLY CLOSING**
周末午膳休息 Closed weekend lunch

浦东新区 **PUDONG**

  ← 🅿 ⟷16 🍴

TEL. 5877 3786

浦东新区富城路33号
浦东香格里拉大酒店2楼

**2F, Pudong Shangri-La Hotel,
33 Fu Cheng Road, Pudong**

www.seventhson.hk

■ 价钱 **PRICE**
午膳 Lunch
套餐 set ¥ 300-400
点菜 à la carte ¥ 450-880
晚膳 Dinner
套餐 set ¥ 500-800
点菜 à la carte ¥ 450-880

■ 营业时间 **OPENING HOURS**
午膳 Lunch 11:30-14:30 (L.O.)
晚膳 Dinner 17:00-22:00 (L.O.)

🍴

家全七福（浦东新区）
SEVENTH SON (PUDONG)

粤菜 · 豪华

Cantonese · Luxury

家全七福在中国、香港和日本等亚洲地区共有七家
食店，秉承在香港的总店致力炮制传统高级粤菜的
精神，此店供应的粤菜不光选料上乘，且绝不卖弄花
巧，纯以天然简单的调味料和扎实细腻的烹调功夫
制作出风味正宗的菜肴。服务员贴心灵巧的服务令用
餐体验生色不少。

Having seven branches spread across China,
Hong Kong and Japan means that this restaurant
group has plenty of experience when it comes
to Cantonese food. Their philosophy here is
to import top class ingredients and allow their
quality to shine through. Located within a luxury
hotel, the restaurant provides a comfortable
setting to go with the views of the Huangpu
River. The experience is further enhanced by the
attentive and professional service.

尚席
SHÀNG-XÍ

中国菜・经典
Chinese・Classic

深棕色凹凸有致的墙壁、别具气派的大理石地面，配上高贵的布艺座椅和偌大的水晶吊灯，营造出法国殖民时期的典雅气息。餐单以广东菜为主，也有少量上海菜和别具特色的新创作，大厨着重味道之余也追求健康，特意减少油和糖的使用，黑松露虾饺皇和层酥红烧肉均是其招牌名菜。

Marble floors, luxurious fabrics and impressive chandeliers add to the elegance of this Chinese restaurant which evokes the colonial style from the time of the French Concession. The menu is largely Cantonese but there are Shanghainese specialities too, as well as some personalised touches from the chef who is committed to creating healthy dishes by using less oil. Try the crispy tofu with barbecue pork, or the shrimp dumpling with truffle.

& 𝐏 ⟳14 ⓘⓣ ⌘
TEL. 2036 1310
浦东新区世纪大道210号
浦东四季酒店2楼
**2F, Four Seasons Pudong,
210 Century Avenue, Pudong**
www.fourseasons.com/pudong

■ 价钱 **PRICE**
午膳 Lunch
套餐 set ¥ 228-680
点菜 à la carte ¥ 300-750
晚膳 Dinner
套餐 set ¥ 680-1,200
点菜 à la carte ¥ 300-750

■ 营业时间 **OPENING HOURS**
午膳 Lunch 11:30-14:15 (L.O.)
晚膳 Dinner 17:30-21:45 (L.O.)

浦东新区 **PUDONG**

207

浦东新区 PUDONG

  🚻 🅿 🍽14 ⚙ 🎷

TEL. 6169 8888

浦东新区花木路1388号
浦东嘉里大酒店2楼

**2F, Kerry Hotel Pudong,
1388 Hua Mu Road, Pudong**

thekerryhotels.com/shanghai

■ **价钱 PRICE**
周末午膳 Weekend lunch
套餐 set ¥ 400-600
点菜 à la carte ¥ 480-1,400
晚膳 Dinner
套餐 set ¥ 500-800
点菜 à la carte ¥ 480-1,400

■ **营业时间 OPENING HOURS**
周末午膳 Weekend lunch
11:30-15:00 (L.O.)
晚膳 Dinner 17:30-22:00 (L.O.)

🍴

扒

THE MEAT

扒房·型格
Steakhouse · Design

餐厅名字说明了一切——主要供应产自澳洲的牛肉。长餐室两边设小型厢座，天花挂满红色牛角状吊灯，别具型格。店内的牛肉均会放于入口处的醒肉房熟成25至31天不等，以达致最佳味道和口感。招牌菜是重1.8公斤的澳洲神户战斧牛排，足够四人享用。酒单选择不俗，包含酒店自酿的手工啤酒。

The gloriously blunt name chosen by the Kerry hotel for their 2nd floor restaurant says it all. This is about beef – mostly Australian – being served in an attractive, masculine room with ox horns as decoration and booths the prized seats. At the entrance you'll see the ageing room where the beef stays for between 25 and 31 days. The signature dish is the 'Nigaloo Tomahawk': 1.8kg of prime rib for four people, which is carved at your table.

惠食佳（浦东新区）
WISCA (PUDONG)

粤菜·时尚

Cantonese · Contemporary décor

源自广州的惠食佳以精致创新的粤菜驰名，后发展至上海。在浦东的这家分店，素白色的环境令心神放松。包厢分布在三楼，四楼的大厅中设有燃木烤鸭炉。海鲜是这儿的主角，此外，还有多款滋味煲仔菜，当中有不少是现煮菜式，故室内总是弥漫着诱人香气。

There's a lighter, whiter colour scheme to this branch from the Wisca group and the atmosphere is comfortable and relaxing. Cantonese seafood dishes are the main draw, but when the casserole dishes are finished off at the tableside and the aroma fills the room you'll regret not ordering one yourself. The restaurant is also equipped with a wood-burning grill to cook its ducks.

♿20 🍽

TEL. 5820 3333

浦东新区陆家嘴东路161号
招商局大厦3-4楼

3-4F, Shanghai Merchants Tower, 161 East Lujiazui Road, Pudong

■ 价钱 **PRICE**
点菜 à la carte ¥ 250-550

■ 营业时间 **OPENING HOURS**
11:00-22:00 (L.O.)

浦东新区 **PUDONG**

HOTELS
酒店

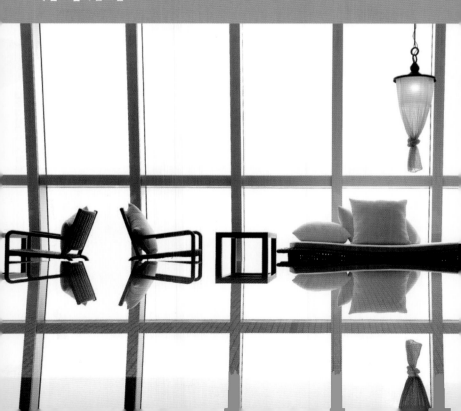

浦东四季
FOUR SEASONS PUDONG

豪华·个性
Luxury · Personalised

于2012年开业的浦东四季酒店，位于陆家嘴金融中心区，占尽地利。时尚典雅的大堂，气氛舒适平静。设于30至39楼的宽敞客房，以米、白、棕三色作主调，搭配风格独特的家具摆设和落地玻璃窗，加上高雅的大理石浴室，设计巧妙。水疗中心、健身房和室内泳池是歇息身心之处。

You get a sense of this luxury hotel's discreet atmosphere and sense of style just by standing in its charming lobby – the hotel occupies floors 30-39 of the tower and opened in 2012. The spacious bedrooms come in white, beige and brown, have floor to ceiling windows, and white marble in their lavish bathrooms. The spa and indoor swimming pool are other features of note.

TEL. 2036 8888

浦东新区世纪大道210号
210 Century Avenue, Pudong
www.fourseasons.com/pudong

172 客房/**Rooms**
15 套房/**Suites**

双人房价格/**Price for 2 persons:**
¥ 2,050-3,250

餐厅推荐/**Recommended restaurants:**
全日 Camelia
尚席 Shàng-Xí

TEL. 2082 9888

浦东新区浦东南路111号
111 South Pudong Road, Pudong

**www.mandarinoriental.com/
shanghai/pudong**

320 客房/**Rooms**
42 套房/**Suites**

双人房价格/**Price for 2 persons:**
¥ 1,700-3,500

餐厅推荐/**Recommended restaurants:**
雍颐庭 Yong Yi Ting

浦东文华东方
MANDARIN ORIENTAL PUDONG

奢华・典雅
Grand Luxury・Elegant

是因为在黄浦江河畔吗？酒店予人的感觉就像夜上海
般奢靡却使人迷醉：大堂的艺术装饰令人目眩；扶手
电梯下，是华丽舒适的水疗中心；拥有宜人园景的露台
小屋实为Qi吧一部分，在这儿与心爱的人浅谈轻酌，可
谓赏心乐事！房间将时尚与东方美完美结合，满眼是
河畔美景。公寓服务适合长期留宿的旅客。

The luxurious bedrooms at this superbly
located hotel in Harbour City come with river
views as standard and blend subtle Oriental
influences with elements of modern design.
Impressive art dominates the lobby; escalators
lead down from here to the sumptuous spa and
Zest restaurant. Long-stay guests enjoy the
same standards at the serviced apartments
next door.

TEL. 2020 1888

浦东新区世纪大道8号
上海国金中心

Shanghai IFC, 8 Century Avenue, Pudong

www.ritzcarlton.cn/shanghaipudong

233 客房/**Rooms**
52 套房/**Suites**

双人房价格/**Price for 2 persons:**
¥ 2,450-3,050

餐厅推荐/**Recommended restaurants:**
金轩　Jin Xuan ⭑○

浦东丽思卡尔顿
THE RITZ-CARLTON PUDONG

奢华 · 现代

Grand Luxury · Modern

屹立在国金中心商场旁边，与东方明珠塔遥遥相对，不论置身大堂还是房间内，都能俯瞰最繁华璀璨的浦江两岸景色。艺术装饰风格的设计中渗透着民初法租界时代的气息，古典雅致。宽敞的房间，拥有大理石浴室和现代设施。高端的泳池、健身房和水疗服务令人流连忘返。Flair顶层酒吧坐拥全上海最佳景致。

It's not just The Ritz-Carlton's terrific location, next to the IFC Mall and facing the Pearl Tower, which makes it stand out. The striking art deco inspired décor and the attention to detail in the service are also hallmarks of this luxurious and elegant hotel. If you want to take in one of the best views in Shanghai, then head up to 'Flair' bar on the top floor.

浦东新区 PUDONG

213

浦东新区 PUDONG

  🏛️

金茂君悦
GRAND HYATT

连锁式・个性
Chain・Personalised

位于有上海地标之称的金茂大厦53至87楼的金茂君悦，装潢时尚且有气派。居高临下，城市的繁华和黄浦江的美景尽收眼底。装潢时尚的客房空間寬敞，床前墙上的唐诗书法，替房间平添了点点书卷与古典味。57楼的泳池、健身房及水疗中心是繁忙过后放松身心的最佳场所。

Renovated in 2013, the Grand Hyatt occupies floors 53-87 of the iconic Jin Mao Tower. The atrium is certainly impressive, as are the views from the lobby and from most of the bedrooms – but for really breathtaking vistas have a cocktail in Cloud 9, the 360° bar on the top floor. The bedrooms are an attractive blend of modern comfort and Chinese design.

TEL. 5049 1234

浦东新区世纪大道88号
金茂大厦

Jin Mao Tower, 88 Century Avenue, Pudong

shanghai.grand.hyatt.com

505 客房/**Rooms**
43 套房/**Suites**
双人房价格/**Price for 2 persons:**
¥ 1,800-6,650

浦东香格里拉
PUDONG SHANGRI-LA

奢华·典雅
Grand Luxury · Elegant

魔都最大型酒店之一的浦东香格里拉由外型时尚的紫金楼和浦江楼组合而成，大概为了呼应两座高楼并肩而立，酒店内的设施也是成双成对：泳池两座、设备完善的健身房两家，其余设施还包括两组按摩浴池、网球场等。紫金楼的客房装潢时尚，浦江楼的客房则较古典，全部房间皆能饱览黄浦江景色。

One of the city's largest hotels is arguably two hotels in one: there's at least two of everything and that includes swimming pools. Bedrooms are divided between two towers: those in the River Wing are more classical in style, while the Grand Tower is home to those of a more contemporary style. All rooms provide great views, as does Jade on 36 bar.

TEL. 6882 8888
浦东新区富城路33号
33 Fu Cheng Road, Pudong
www.shangri-la.com/pudong

885 客房/**Rooms**
66 套房/**Suites**
双人房价格/**Price for 2 persons:**
¥ 1,188-3,800

餐厅推荐/Recommended restaurants:
家全七福 Seventh Son ⑩

浦东新区 **PUDONG**

浦东新区 PUDONG

TEL. 6888 1234

浦东新区世纪大道100号
上海环球金融中心

**Shanghai World Financial Center,
100 Century Avenue, Pudong**

parkhyattshanghai.com

160 客房/**Rooms**
13 套房/**Suites**

双人房价格/**Price for 2 persons:**
¥ 1,700-3,500

柏悦
PARK HYATT

豪华・型格
Luxury・Design

位于上海环球金融中心79至93楼的柏悦酒店，由著
名设计师季裕堂设计，气氛祥和、装潢高雅。房间沿
用极简主义概念，以简单的线条、清雅的素材、现代
艺术结合中国文化塑造出时尚、简约与舒适的感觉。
公共空间如起居室、音乐室及92楼的老上海酒吧是
消闲的好去处。想健康点，不妨参与太极庭院活动。

Park Hyatt occupies one of the tallest
buildings in the city and its designer's aim
was to create a 'modern Chinese mansion' by
mixing contemporary art and Chinese culture.
Bedrooms come with high ceilings, large
bathrooms and great views. Equal thought has
gone into the public areas, like the Music Room
and the Shanghai Lounge. On weekdays you
can take tai chi lessons.

卓美亚喜玛拉雅

JUMEIRAH HIMALAYAS

商务 · 独特

Business · Unique

酒店位处展览馆旁,设计出自日籍建筑师手笔,大堂设计独特,与新潮奇异的入口相映成趣。客房高雅而富现代感,落地窗户让窗外景色尽收眼底。餐膳选择丰富,从寿司、咖啡店至上海菜式式俱备。酒店大堂的凉亭每晚有现场音乐演奏。水疗中心融合中国的养生概念,设备完善。

Designed by a Japanese architect, this luxury hotel boasts a very original design and a quirky modern façade. Bedrooms are modern and stylish and brightened by floor to ceiling glass windows. Dining options abound, from sushi and teppanyaki to Shanghainese. There is a pagoda in the lobby where you can enjoy live music. Talise, the Chinese spa, is impressively equipped.

TEL. 3858 0888

浦东新区梅花路1108号

1108 Mei Hua Road, Pudong

www.jumeirah.com/en/hotels-resorts/shanghai

337 客房/**Rooms**
66 套房/**Suites**

双人房价格/**Price for 2 persons:**
¥ 1,000-4,000

餐厅推荐/**Recommended restaurants:**
迷上海 Shang-High Cuisine ✿

浦东新区 **PUDONG**

217

浦东新区 PUDONG

♿ ⬳ 🅿 🚗 ⅏ 🏋 🖼 🧖 🏋

TEL. 6169 8888

浦东新区花木路1388号
1388 Hua Mu Road, Pudong
thekerryhotels.com/shanghai

541 客房/**Rooms**
33 套房/**Suites**

双人房价格/**Price for 2 persons:**
￥1,388-2,488

餐厅推荐/**Recommended restaurants:**
扒 The Meat ⅏

🏠🏠🏠

浦东嘉里
KERRY PUDONG

连锁式・个性
Chain・Personalised

酒店内占地三层的大型健身俱乐部，拥有完备的健康休闲设施：水疗中心、网球场等，还有供儿童戏耍的探险乐园，可谓各适其适、老幼咸宜。客房以暖色调、优质物料和高雅的装饰布置，宽敞的空间与特大的睡床，尽是舒适，适合整家子欢度假期。免费迷你酒吧内还提供手工啤酒。

It may be close to the Expo centre (SNIEC) but the large swimming pool, vast fitness centre, spa, tennis court, and kids' Adventure Zone make this Shangri-La managed hotel as popular with families as it is with business types. Bedrooms are bigger than average and the free minibar includes some of the hotel's homemade beer, which may help de-stress some parents.

浦东新区 **PUDONG**

索引
INDEX

星级餐厅
STARRED RESTAURANTS

必比登美食推介餐厅
BIB GOURMAND RESTAURANTS

———————

😋

餐厅列表
INDEX OF RESTAURANTS

餐厅 — 以菜式分类
RESTAURANTS BY CUISINE TYPE

_____

沪菜/SHANGHAINESE

美国菜/AMERICAN

烧烤/BARBECUE

老干杯/Kanpai Classic ⑪◯　　　　　　　　　　　　68

粤菜/CANTONESE

喜粤8号(南京东路)/Canton 8 (East Nanjing Road) ⑪◯ Ⓝ　56

喜粤8号(汝南街)/Canton 8 (Runan Street) ✿✿　　　28

翡翠酒家(黄浦)/Crystal Jade (Huangpu) ⍟　　　　43

翡翠酒家(静安)/Crystal Jade (Jingan) ⑪◯　　　　122

文兴酒家/Four Seasons ⍟　　　　　　　　　　118

恒悦轩(浦东新区)/Hang Yuen Hin (Pudong) ⑪◯　202

恒悦轩(徐汇)/Hang Yuen Hin (Xuhui) ⑪◯　　　172

御宝轩/Imperial Treasure ✿✿　　　　　　　29

吉品轩/Ji Pin Court ✿ Ⓝ　　　　　　　　　159

金轩/Jin Xuan ⑪◯　　　　　　　　　　　203

逸荟/La Société ⑪◯　　　　　　　　　　　69

利苑(浦东新区)/Lei Garden (Pudong) ✿　　　196

利苑(徐汇)/Lei Garden (Xuhui) ✿　　　　　161

月半鸭/Phat Duck ⑪◯ Ⓝ　　　　　　　　151

皇朝会/Royal China Club ⑪◯　　　　　　　80

家全七福(静安)/Seventh Son (Jingan) ✿　　115

家全七福(浦东新区)/Seventh Son (Pudong) ⑪◯　206

夏宫/Summer Palace ⑪◯　　　　　　　　128

唐阁/T'ang Court ✿✿　　　　　　　　　32

蔚景阁/Wei Jing Ge ⑪◯　　　　　　　　　87

惠食佳(静安)/Wisca (Jingan) ⑪◯　　　　　130

惠食佳(浦东新区)/Wisca (Pudong) ⑪◯　　　209

馨源楼/Xin Yuan Lou ⑪◯　　　　　　　　89

逸龙阁/Yi Long Court ✿✿　　　　　　　33

烧味/CANTONESE ROAST MEAT

鹅夫人(闵行)/Madam Goose (Minhang) ✿　　162

潮州菜/CHAO ZHOU

菁禧荟/Amazing Chinese Cuisine ✿　　　　143

中国菜/CHINESE

时尚中国菜/CHINESE CONTEMPORARY

点心/DIAN XIN

时尚欧陆菜/EUROPEAN CONTEMPORARY

法国菜/FRENCH

时尚法国菜/FRENCH CONTEMPORARY

有私人厢房的餐厅
INDEX OF RESTAURANTS WITH PRIVATE ROOMS

酒店列表
INDEX OF HOTELS